MACMILLA

English

DICTIONARY

FOR ADVANCED LEARNERS

Workbook

ADRIAN UNDERHILL

MACMILLAN

Macmillan Education
Between Towns Road, Oxford OX4 3PP
A division of Macmillan Publishers Limited
Companies and representatives throughout the world

ISBN 0 333 96689 9 (British English edition)
ISBN 0 333 96690 2 (American English edition)

Designed by Lenn Darroux
Cover design based on an original design by Conor Mangat of
Boag Associates, London

Author's acknowledgements
Many thanks for the help and assistance of Kati Süle
throughout the preparation of this workbook.

The author and publishers would like to thank the following
for permission to reproduce their material:
Virgin Books (an imprint of Virgin Publishing Ltd) for the
extract 'The Memory Man' from Now! That's What I Call
Urban Myths by Phil Healey and Rich Glanvill; Private Eye for
the extract 'Funny Old World', no 1029, 1-14 June 2001;
New Scientist for the extract 'Into the Abyss', no 2284, 31
March 2001.

The publishers would like to thank Chris Dawson for his
contribution.

Whilst every effort has been made to locate the owners of
copyright, in some cases this has been unsuccessful. The
publishers apologise for any infringement or failure to
acknowledge the original sources and will be glad to include
any necessary correction in subsequent printings.

Printed and bound in Great Britain by Scotprint

2006 2005 2004 2003 2002
10 9 8 7 6 5 4 3 2 1

Welcome!

This workbook accompanies the new *Macmillan English Dictionary*. The special features of the *Macmillan English Dictionary* are designed to give you more information and to make it easier to use:

▶ Red words show you which words are the most frequent and most useful to learn

▶ Extra information is given on how to use these frequent words

▶ Menus for longer entries take you more quickly to the meaning you want

▶ Meanings are illustrated with real-life examples

Being able to use a dictionary well is a great pleasure and will bring independence and confidence to your language studies. This workbook will help you to get the best out of your dictionary, and by working through these activities you will be able to:

▶ find words quickly

▶ learn how to find pronunciation and stress

▶ use grammatical information

▶ find and explore meanings

▶ learn which words are used together

▶ choose the right word for the context

Explanations and examples are followed by activities to practise your dictionary and language skills. You can work through the exercises in any order, in class or for self-study, and check your answers in the key at the end.

The more you use the dictionary the more you will learn. We hope that you will enjoy these activities and add an important new resource to your learning!

Contents

Finding words in the dictionary

1 Alphabetical ordering

The words, compounds and abbreviations in this dictionary are in simple alphabetical order. For example, the 14 entries starting from *taxpayer* are listed in the following order:

> **taxpayer** /ˈtæksˌpeɪə/ noun [C] ★★ someone who pays tax, especially tax on income: *Whenever the government messes up, it's the taxpayer who has to foot the bill.*

> **'tax reˌlief** noun [U] a reduction in tax that you are allowed for a particular reason
> **'tax reˌturn** noun [C] an official document for giving details of your income so that the government can calculate the amount of tax you have to pay
> **'tax ˌshelter** noun [C] somewhere you can invest your money without having to pay tax on the profits
> **'tax ˌyear** noun [C] a period of 12 months that is used for calculating taxes
> **TB** /ˌtiː ˈbiː/ noun [U] tuberculosis: a serious infectious disease that mainly affects the lungs
> **TBA** abbrev to be announced: used for saying that you will be told something at a later time because it has not yet been decided
> **T-ball** /ˈtiː ˌbɔːl/ noun [U] a form of baseball played in the US by young children in which the ball is not thrown but is placed on a special stick so that you can hit it easily
> **T-bone steak** /ˌtiː bəʊn ˈsteɪk/ noun [C] a thick slice of BEEF containing a bone shaped like the letter T
> **tbs** or **tbsp** abbrev tablespoon
> **T cell** /ˈtiː sel/ noun [C] a type of white blood cell that helps the body fight disease
> **TCP** /ˌtiː siː ˈpiː/ *trademark* a liquid used for treating minor infections such as those in cuts, sore throats etc
> **TCP/IP** /ˌtiː siː ˌpiː aɪ ˈpiː/ abbrev *computing* transmission control protocol/Internet protocol: a set of rules used by all computers on the Internet that allow them to communicate with each other
> **tea** /tiː/ noun ★★★
>   **1** [U] a hot brown drink made by pouring boiling water onto the dried leaves of the tea bush. The leaves are called **tea leaves** and can be bought in small paper bags called **tea bags** that are put into a cup or **teapot**: *Do*

▶ Exercise 1

Find the word in each column which is not in alphabetical order. Put it in its correct place, as in the example.

a	b	c
ascent	GR8	the KGB
prominent	e-book	kick
collide	intimidating	oil
curious	jaw	OHP
exhilarating	safeguard	oil rig
thorn	yawn	oily

d	e	f
VP	knuckle	stud
voting booth	KO	studio
voucher	kph	student
vow	koala	study
voyage	kohlrabi	stuff
vulture	kung fu	stumble

▶ Exercise 2

Put the words in each column in alphabetical order.

a
write-off	*world-famous*
wrong	_____
world-famous	_____
wreckage	_____
WP	_____
wrapping paper	_____

b
perspective	_____
piggy bank	_____
persist	_____
PG	_____
phone number	_____
playground	_____

c
ID card	_____
round-trip	_____
press-up	_____
honeymoon	_____
evacuate	_____
queen bee	_____

▶ Exercise 3

Put the words in the box in alphabetical order. Check your answers in the dictionary.

to	toast	TLC	toasting fork	toad-in-the-hole	
to and fro	TM	toaster	T-junction	toad	
toadstool	TMT	toady	tizzy	TNT	toastie

a _tizzy_   i _____

b _____   j _____

c _____   k _____

d _____   l _____

e _____   m _____

f _____   n _____

g _____   o _____

h _____   p _____

2 Guide words

There are two guide words at the top of each page that show the first and last words on that dictionary page. These help you to find words quickly.

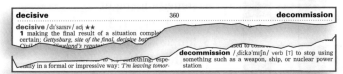

decisive   360   decommission

decisive /dɪˈsaɪsɪv/ adj ★★
1 making the final result of a situation comple
certain: *Gettysburg, site of the final, decisive ba*

decommission /ˌdiːkəˈmɪʃn/ verb [T] to stop using
something such as a weapon, ship, or nuclear power
station

▶ Exercise 4

Which of these words (a–k) will be found on the page that has guide words *decisive* .... *decommission*? Tick the correct column.

	Yes	No
a deconstruct	☐	✔
b the Declaration of Independence	☐	☐
c deckchair	☐	☐
d decision	☐	☐
e decoration	☐	☐
f decode	☐	☐
g decline	☐	☐
h decompress	☐	☐
i decide	☐	☐
j decompose	☐	☐
k decent	☐	☐

▶ Exercise 5

On which of these pages would you expect to find the words in the box? Write them under the correct guide words.

stout	strain	stranger	storey	straight
strand	straighten	story	straight away	
stove	strap	straight-faced		

a

store card   1414   stow

stout   _____

_____   _____

b

stowage   1415   straightforward

_____   _____

_____   _____

c

straightjacket   1416   strap

_____   _____

_____   _____

▶ Exercise 6

Look at the guide words. Think of three words that you would expect to find on these pages. Then check in the dictionary.

a

leg   814   legislative

legal   _____   _____

b

love bite   852   low

_____   _____

c

journal   774   judge

_____   _____

d

user-friendly   1585   U-turn

_____   _____

▶ **Exercise 7**

The letter J

Most of the clues and some of the answers in this crossword are taken from the letter J in the dictionary. If you need help, look up the word in red.

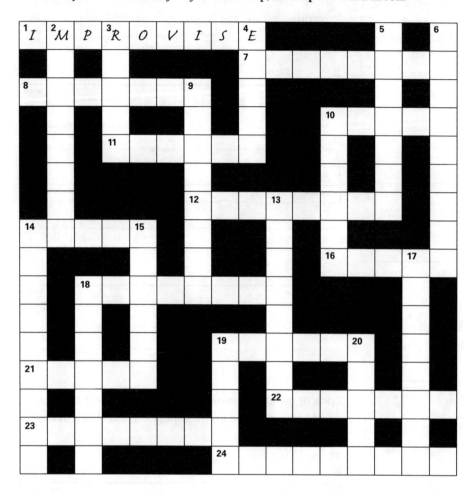

DOWN

2 At a wedding, two people are joined in _____ . (8)

3 'Hang on! We're not quite _____ to leave yet.' (5)

4 You can jab something with a narrow object, your finger or your _____ . (5)

5 To criticize someone in a way that shows you think you are better than they are is to _____ judgment over them. (5,2)

6 Small attractive objects used for decorating, for example a Christmas tree. (9)

9 A _____ is a dried pea, cut in half. (5,3)

10 A child excited about doing something might _____ and down. (4, 2)

13 Jungle is a music that developed in the 1990s from hardcore _____ . (3,5)

14 Your jaw is the _____ of your face. (5,4)

15 If you follow something to the _____ , you do exactly what you are told to do. (6)

17 Jodhpurs are _____ worn for horse-riding. (8)

18 'And they all lived _____ ever after.' (7)

19 A true Cockney is said to be someone who is born within the _____ of Bow Bells. (5)

20 Another name for a juicer is a _____ squeezer. (5)

ACROSS

1 In jazz music, the musicians often _____ . (9)

7 Jeering is rude _____ at someone in a public place. (8)

8 A jet engine _____ power from air and burning fuel. (7)

10 A group of military officers that governs a country, usually without having been elected. (5)

11 Jaundice is an illness that makes the skin and the white part of the eyes become _____ . (6)

12 Something really good has _____ for people to feel jubilant. (2,6)

14 In a joint degree, two subjects are studied to the same _____ . (5)

16 A joiner makes the wooden _____ of buildings. (5)

18 A Jacuzzi is full of _____ . (3,5)

19 You can jam a radio _____ by broadcasting another on the same wavelength. (6)

21 A Japanese lantern is made of _____ . (5)

22 A juror is _____ of a jury. (1,6)

23 Judaism is the name of a _____ . (8)

24 Jiggery-pokery is _____ behaviour intended to trick people. (9)

3 Checking spellings

You can use the dictionary to check how a word is spelled. If you are not sure of the spelling of a word, write down the letters that you do know and guess the others. Then check in your dictionary. With practice you will become good at guessing and quick at finding spellings.

▶ **Exercise 8**

This exercise gives you some practice in guessing missing letters in words.

1 First decide if the missing letters are vowels or consonants.
2 Next write down the letters you think might be possible.
3 Then check the spelling in the dictionary.

a lab_y_rinth   e bel___eve   i stomac___

b p___antom   f bankrup___cy   j mousta___he

c uncons___ious   g p___ece   k conscie___ce

d lac___uer   h rest___urant   l proce___d

4 Alternative spellings

Sometimes there is more than one way to spell a word in English. There may also be differences between British and American spellings. The dictionary shows these like this:

despatch /dɪˈspætʃ/ another spelling of **dispatch**[1]

analyze /ˈænəˌlaɪz/ the Am E spelling of **analyse**

▶ **Exercise 9**

1 Use the dictionary to find the alternative spellings and write these in the first column.
2 If the alternative is American or British English, tick the second or third column.

	1 Write the alternative spelling.	2 Is the alternative American English?	3 Is the alternative British English?
a chamomile	camomile	☐	☐
b defense	defence	☐	✔
c ikon		☐	☐
d tire		☐	☐
e racquet		☐	☐

	1 Write the alternative spelling.	2 Is the alternative American English?	3 Is the alternative British English?
f swop		☐	☐
g jewelry		☐	☐
h hippy		☐	☐
i baptise		☐	☐
j enquiry		☐	☐
k unrecognisable		☐	☐
l okay		☐	☐
m program		☐	☐
n nosey		☐	☐
o czar		☐	☐
p moisturise		☐	☐
q color		☐	☐
r catalog		☐	☐
s encyclopaedia		☐	☐

5 Abbreviations

▶ **Exercise 10**

Use the dictionary to find the usual abbreviations for these words.

a department   _dept_

b year   _____

c company   _____

d limited   _____

e not applicable   _____

f street   _____

g or nearest offer   _____

h minimum   _____

i date of birth   _____

j care of   _____

Interesting facts

The seven most common words in written English are *the, of, and, a, in, to* and *it*. These words make up almost 20% of every text you read, which is astonishing when you consider how many hundreds of thousands of English words are available.

Red words and black words

Open the dictionary at any page. Notice that some headwords are red and some are black. The red words are the frequently used words in English.

▶ **Exercise 11**

Look at a few of the red words in the dictionary. Notice how many stars follow each red word.

_____

The words that are followed by ★ are frequent words, the ones that are followed by ★★ are more frequent, and the words that have ★★★ next to them are the most frequently used words in English.

▶ **Exercise 12**

Turn to pages 1026–1027 in the dictionary. How many red words are there on these pages? What are these words?

_____

_____

_____

_____

Remember that these red words are the most common words in English. These are in general the words native speakers use every day to express themselves in speaking or writing. All the other words in the dictionary are in black. These are less frequent words and you are more likely to need them when you are reading than when you are speaking.

▶ **Exercise 13**

Four words in the following paragraphs are not red. Guess which they are and check them in the dictionary.

A survey carried out has found some shocking lapses of etiquette in the messages passed around by people under 20.

Many youngsters prefer to send e-mail rather than write a letter, but the survey reveals that most have no conception of what counts as proper manners when penning a digital missive.

▶ **Exercise 14**

Look at pages 555–565 in the dictionary. What do you notice about the length of the entries for red words?

_____

_____

_____

_____

You may have noticed that:

1 the entries for red words are generally longer. This is because frequent words often have more meanings.
2 the entries for red words contain more information about usage so that you can learn how to use them yourself.

The most frequent words are in red in the dictionary. The 2500 most frequent words have ★★★. The next most frequent 2500 (2501–5000) words have ★★ and the next most frequent 2500 (5001–7500) words have ★.

Remember!
The red words are the most frequently used words in English.

Introducing concordances

The World English Corpus is an up-to-date database containing over 200 million words of real-life written and spoken English. It shows how words are <u>actually used</u> and what meanings they have. This database was used to make the *Macmillan English Dictionary*. Computer software allows us to show every occurrence of a word, with the words before it and after it, as in the example for the word *jam* below. This is called a *concordance*, and as you can see the concordance shows examples of how each word is used in a sentence, the grammatical construction it is part of, and the other words that are used with it.

The following concordance examples are taken from the World English Corpus. In the activities you use these concordance examples to study different meanings of the word (just as the authors of the dictionary did). In each case you can use the dictionary to help and to check your answers.

▶ **Exercise 15**

Look at this concordance for the word *jam*. Notice the different meanings it has.

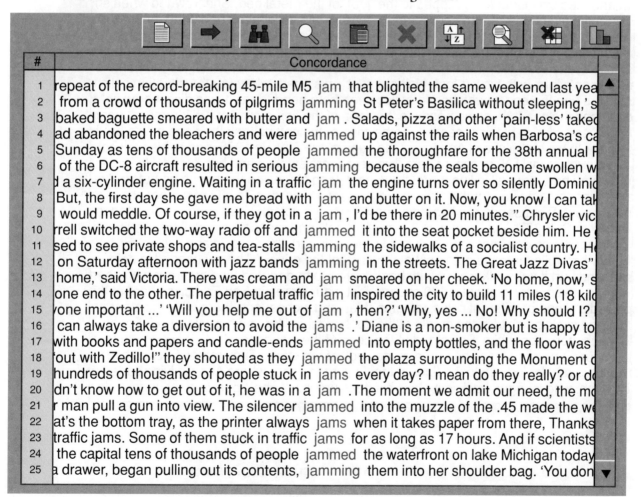

#	Concordance
1	repeat of the record-breaking 45-mile M5 jam that blighted the same weekend last yea
2	from a crowd of thousands of pilgrims jamming St Peter's Basilica without sleeping,' s
3	baked baguette smeared with butter and jam . Salads, pizza and other 'pain-less' taked
4	ad abandoned the bleachers and were jammed up against the rails when Barbosa's ca
5	Sunday as tens of thousands of people jammed the thoroughfare for the 38th annual F
6	of the DC-8 aircraft resulted in serious jamming because the seals become swollen w
7	d a six-cylinder engine. Waiting in a traffic jam the engine turns over so silently Dominic
8	But, the first day she gave me bread with jam and butter on it. Now, you know I can tak
9	would meddle. Of course, if they got in a jam , I'd be there in 20 minutes." Chrysler vic
10	rrell switched the two-way radio off and jammed it into the seat pocket beside him. He
11	sed to see private shops and tea-stalls jamming the sidewalks of a socialist country. H
12	on Saturday afternoon with jazz bands jamming in the streets. The Great Jazz Divas"
13	home,' said Victoria. There was cream and jam smeared on her cheek. 'No home, now,' s
14	one end to the other. The perpetual traffic jam inspired the city to build 11 miles (18 kilo
15	one important ...' 'Will you help me out of jam , then?' 'Why, yes ... No! Why should I?
16	can always take a diversion to avoid the jams .' Diane is a non-smoker but is happy to
17	with books and papers and candle-ends jammed into empty bottles, and the floor was
18	'out with Zedillo!" they shouted as they jammed the plaza surrounding the Monument
19	hundreds of thousands of people stuck in jams every day? I mean do they really? or d
20	dn't know how to get out of it, he was in a jam .The moment we admit our need, the m
21	r man pull a gun into view. The silencer jammed into the muzzle of the .45 made the w
22	at's the bottom tray, as the printer always jams when it takes paper from there, Thanks
23	traffic jams. Some of them stuck in traffic jams for as long as 17 hours. And if scientists
24	the capital tens of thousands of people jammed the waterfront on lake Michigan today
25	a drawer, began pulling out its contents, jamming them into her shoulder bag. 'You don

Interesting facts

The most common 2500 words in English are marked with ★★★ in the dictionary. These words account for approximately 80% of all text.

► **Exercise 16**

Look at the concordance. Study the examples of the word *foot* in use and answer the questions. Check in the dictionary.

a How many meanings are there and what are they?

_____

_____

_____

_____

b Which meaning do you think is the most frequent in English?

_____

c And which meaning is the least frequent?

_____

Remember that the dictionary shows the most frequent meaning first and the least frequent meaning last.

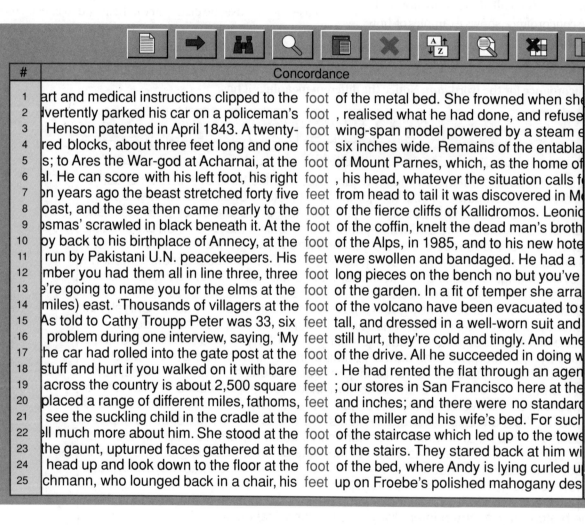

#	Concordance
1	art and medical instructions clipped to the **foot** of the metal bed. She frowned when she
2	dvertently parked his car on a policeman's **foot** , realised what he had done, and refuse
3	Henson patented in April 1843. A twenty- **foot** wing-span model powered by a steam e
4	red blocks, about three feet long and one **foot** six inches wide. Remains of the entabla
5	s; to Ares the War-god at Acharnai, at the **foot** of Mount Parnes, which, as the home of
6	al. He can score with his left foot, his right **foot** , his head, whatever the situation calls f
7	on years ago the beast stretched forty five **feet** from head to tail it was discovered in M
8	oast, and the sea then came nearly to the **foot** of the fierce cliffs of Kallidromos. Leoni
9	smas' scrawled in black beneath it. At the **foot** of the coffin, knelt the dead man's broth
10	oy back to his birthplace of Annecy, at the **foot** of the Alps, in 1985, and to his new hote
11	run by Pakistani U.N. peacekeepers. His **feet** were swollen and bandaged. He had a
12	mber you had them all in line three, three **foot** long pieces on the bench no but you've
13	e're going to name you for the elms at the **foot** of the garden. In a fit of temper she arra
14	miles) east. 'Thousands of villagers at the **foot** of the volcano have been evacuated to s
15	As told to Cathy Troupp Peter was 33, six **feet** tall, and dressed in a well-worn suit and
16	problem during one interview, saying, 'My **feet** still hurt, they're cold and tingly. And whe
17	he car had rolled into the gate post at the **foot** of the drive. All he succeeded in doing w
18	stuff and hurt if you walked on it with bare **feet** . He had rented the flat through an agen
19	across the country is about 2,500 square **feet** ; our stores in San Francisco here at the
20	placed a range of different miles, fathoms, **feet** and inches; and there were no standard
21	see the suckling child in the cradle at the **foot** of the miller and his wife's bed. For such
22	ell much more about him. She stood at the **foot** of the staircase which led up to the towe
23	the gaunt, upturned faces gathered at the **foot** of the stairs. They stared back at him wi
24	head up and look down to the floor at the **foot** of the bed, where Andy is lying curled u
25	chmann, who lounged back in a chair, his **feet** up on Froebe's polished mahogany des

Interesting facts

Before computerized corpora became available, dictionary editors used the approach pioneered by Dr Johnson in the 18th century, basing their description of the language on large collections of *citations* (= short extracts from texts), collected by human readers and showing a particular word or phrase in context.

Pronunciation and stress

1 Pronunciation guide

The dictionary gives the pronunciation of words using the international phonetic alphabet (IPA). Each symbol always represents the same sound. You can find a list of phonetic symbols on page 1692 of the dictionary.

▶ **Exercise 17**

Look up the pronunciation guide in the dictionary and answer these questions.

a How many consonants are there? _____

b How many vowels and diphthongs are there? _____

Look at the final eight symbols in the list of vowels and diphthongs. Notice that each one is made up of two symbols. These sounds are called *diphthongs* and are made by gliding from the first sound to the second.

▶ **Exercise 18**

Notice that some of the phonetic symbols are the same as the letters of the English alphabet (e.g. /m/ and /e/) and some are different (e.g. /ŋ/ and /æ/). List five of each in the table below.

same as a letter in the English alphabet	different from any letter in the English alphabet
v	dʒ

▶ **Exercise 19**

Write down the example words for the following sounds. Then find another word in the dictionary that contains this sound.

		example word	another word
a	/æ/	bad	ran
b	/eɪ/		
c	/j/		
d	/ʌ/		
e	/θ/		
f	/əʊ/		
g	/ʃ/		
h	/ɔː/		

▶ **Exercise 20**

Study the example words in the pronunciation guide. How do you say them? Check your pronunciation of these words with your teacher, or by listening to the *Macmillan English Dictionary CD-ROM*.

2 Using the phonetic key

▶ **Exercise 21**

Put the words in the box in the correct column according to their vowel sound. Check in the dictionary.

put   oar   fool   thorn   cool   do   foot
floor   bush   goods

1 cook /ʊ/	2 food /uː/	3 door /ɔː/
put		

▶ **Exercise 22**

Look up these words in the dictionary. Copy out the phonetic spelling in your own handwriting.

a one   wʌn _____
b through   _____
c ache   _____
d mall   _____
e hair   _____
f kick   _____
g song   _____
h while   _____
i bathe   _____
j toss   _____

▶ **Exercise 23**

Circle the word that is in the wrong group. Indicate with an arrow which group it belongs to.

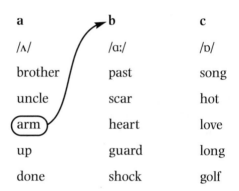

a	b	c
/ʌ/	/ɑː/	/ɒ/
brother	past	song
uncle	scar	hot
(arm)	heart	love
up	guard	long
done	shock	golf

▶ **Exercise 24**

The spelling *ough* has several possible pronunciations. Put these words in the correct column according to the pronunciation of *ough* in each one.

cough	bough	brought	enough	plough
through	dough	bought	tough	thought
fought	rough	drought	though	

/ʌ/	/ɔː/	/aʊ/	/əʊ/	/uː/
cough	___	___	___	___
___	___	___	___	___
___	___	___	___	
___				

▶ **Exercise 25**

Complete the sentences with a correct word from the box. Check your answers in the dictionary.

ˈpræktɪkli	kæmˈpeɪn	ɔːlˈðəʊ	ˈpɔɪznəs
ˌreprɪˈzentətɪv	səˈfɪstɪˌkeɪtɪd		

a The party expected an easy ___campaign___ with many victories in the next elections.
b He was a union _____ for 14 years so he knows a great deal about the industry.
c I've been saving £5 a week for _____ the whole year but my savings still come next to nothing.
d Technical equipment is more _____ today and requires more experience.
e _____ he spoke English fluently he never completely mastered it nor lost his accent.
f The only _____ snake in this county is the viper.

3 Silent letters

English spellings sometimes contain letters that are not pronounced. For example, 'b' in *lamb*, 'n' in *hymn* or 'l' in *walk*.

▶ **Exercise 26**

Use your dictionary to find the silent letters in the words. Circle the silent letter in each word.

a (h)onest   e knee   i autumn
b comb   f salmon   j island
c palm   g psyche   k knob
d gnome   h pneumonia   l fasten

4 Saying abbreviations

There are three ways of saying an abbreviation in English:

1 say each letter separately. For example, CCTV /ˌsiː siː tiː viː/;
2 say it as an acronym (i.e. make a word out of the letters). For example, WAP /wæp/;
3 say the full form of the word. For example, St /striːt/.

The dictionary tells you the correct way.

SLR /ˌes el ˈɑː/ *abbrev* single lens reflex: a type of camera that allows you to see exactly what will appear in the photograph when you look through the VIEWFINDER

▶ **Exercise 27**

Use the dictionary to check how to say each of these abbreviations.
Tick the correct column. Then write the full forms for the abbreviations.

	1 say each letter separately	2 say it as an acronym	3 say the full form of the word	write the full form of the word
a pm	✓	☐	☐	_post meridiem_
b attn	☐	☐	☐	_____
c BC	☐	☐	☐	_____
d DC	☐	☐	☐	_____
e INSET	☐	☐	☐	_____
f m8	☐	☐	☐	_____
g MOR	☐	☐	☐	_____
h SWALK	☐	☐	☐	_____
i tsp.	☐	☐	☐	_____
j wk	☐	☐	☐	_____

5 Stress in English words

A syllable is a unit of sounds containing either one vowel (*I*, *eye*), or a vowel and one or more consonants (*my*, *I'm*, *size*). The pronunciation of a word therefore consists of one or more syllables.

▶ **Exercise 28**

Tick the correct box for each word according to the number of syllables it has.

	1 syllable	2 syllables	3 syllables	4 syllables	5 syllables
a fourteen	☐	✓	☐	☐	☐
b fortunate	☐	☐	☐	☐	☐
c fortunately	☐	☐	☐	☐	☐
d force	☐	☐	☐	☐	☐
e famous	☐	☐	☐	☐	☐
f unfortunate	☐	☐	☐	☐	☐
g unfortunately	☐	☐	☐	☐	☐
h four	☐	☐	☐	☐	☐
i formula	☐	☐	☐	☐	☐

A spoken word is recognized not only by its pronunciation but also by its stress pattern. Every word of more than one syllable has a fixed stress pattern which means that one of the syllables is spoken with more force. The dictionary shows this by putting ' before the syllable in the phonetic spelling.

except[1] /ɪk'sept/ function word ★★★

Longer words may have two stressed syllables, in which case one is stronger than the other. The stronger is called primary stress and it is shown with '. The less strong is called secondary stress and it is shown like this , .

examination /ɪɡˌzæmɪ'neɪʃn/ noun ★★★

▶ **Exercise 29**

Mark the primary and secondary stress in these words, using ' for the primary and , for the secondary.

a 'coverage
b neighbour
c tomorrow
d complementary
e arrangement
f atmosphere
g between
h surprise
i occur
j expert
k photographic
l acceleration

▶ **Exercise 30**

Put the words in the box into the correct column according to the stress pattern in each.

sixty   sixteen   correct   fantasy
fantastic   advertisement   advertise   inform
information   educate   education   photography
photo   photographic   image   imagine
significant   banana

a ☐☐
sixty

b ☐☐

c ☐☐☐

d ☐☐☐

e ☐☐☐☐

f ☐☐☐☐

▶ **Exercise 31**

1 Underline the words in this passage that contain more than one syllable.

Robyn adored the way beautiful living pictures could be created outdoors with just some foresight and imagination and a knowledge of simple plants. It had been a slow process, of course, but gradually her reputation had grown and she had gained a singular name for creative, imaginative work.

2 Now write each of the words you have underlined in one of the columns below according to whether its primary stress is on the first, second, third or fourth syllable. Check in the dictionary.

a
first syllable

b
second syllable
adored

c
third syllable

d
fourth syllable

6 Words that can be both nouns and verbs

A characteristic of English is that many words can be used both as nouns and verbs with the same spelling but with different word stress. Where the stress is different in the noun and verb, the stress is usually on the first syllable for the noun and the second syllable for the verb. For example:

> **object**[1] /ˈɒbdʒɪkt/ noun [C] ★★★

> **object**[2] /əbˈdʒekt/ verb [I/T] ★★ to be opposed to

▶ **Exercise 32**

The words below can be both nouns and verbs. Fill in the table according to which syllable is stressed in the noun and in the verb. Use your dictionary to check.

□ □	□ □
a increase _noun_	_verb_
b export	
c transfer	
d import	
e suspect	
f record	
g progress	
h convict	
i permit	

Notice that in the words above the primary stress is always on the first syllable when the words are used as nouns. When they are used as verbs, the primary stress is on the second syllable.

7 Stress in compounds

Some compounds are written as single words. These are shown as headwords in the dictionary. The pronunciation and stress for these words are given in the normal way. For example:

> **housework** / ˈhaʊsˌwɜːk / noun [U] ★ the work that you do to keep your house clean and tidy

Other compounds are written as separate words, for example *black belt*, or as hyphenated words, for example *sister-in-law*. Usually the main stress of these compounds is on the first word but the dictionary will tell you by showing the stress marks like this:

> ˈblack ˌbelt noun [C] the highest level of skill in some types of MARTIAL ART such as JUDO or KARATE, represented

> ˈsister-in-ˌlaw noun [C] **1** the sister of your husband or wife. The brother of your husband or wife is your brother-in-law.

▶ **Exercise 33**

Use the dictionary to identify and mark the primary and secondary stress in these compounds.

a ˌice ˈcream
b jet lag
c matchbox
d floppy disk
e bookmark
f ice rink
g roadside
h mobile phone
i workload

Interesting facts

The most common noun in all forms of English is *time*.

Grammar information

1 Word classes

Each headword has a label that shows its word class, for example, *noun*, *adj* (= adjective), *phrasal vb* (= phrasal verb) and *adverb*. A list of these labels is shown at the beginning of the dictionary.

suggest /səˈdʒest/ (verb) [T] ★★★
1 to offer an idea or a plan for someone

▶ **Exercise 34**

Write a correct word class from the box next to each word. Then check in the dictionary.

| noun | conjunction | interjection |
| preposition | adjective | |

a scenery   *noun*   h during   _____

b hello   _____   i indoor   _____

c with   _____   j please   _____

d convinced   _____   k whereas   _____

e whether   _____   l provided   _____

f frail   _____   m blessing   _____

g honey   _____   n despite   _____

▶ **Exercise 35**

Many words in English can belong to more than one word class. Look up the word *back*. Notice that it can be an adverb (back¹), an adjective (back²), a noun (back³) and a verb (back⁴). What is the connection between the meanings?

_____

_____

_____

_____

_____

▶ **Exercise 36**

Read the sentences and study the underlined words.

1 Write the word class of the underlined word in the first column.
2 Now find the word in the dictionary and write the headword and its number in the second column.

	word class	headword
a Their <u>wages</u> are the lowest in town.	*noun*	*wage¹*
b Airlines <u>face</u> enormous losses.	_____	_____
c She came <u>second</u> in the tournament.	_____	_____
d The river is in the <u>east</u> of the town.	_____	_____
e Of course we believe we are fighting for a <u>just</u> cause.	_____	_____
f We're having a <u>do</u> this evening because it's our last time together.	_____	_____
g I'm <u>halfway</u> through the book.	_____	_____
h <u>Morning</u>, George. You're early.	_____	_____

▶ **Exercise 37**

Look in your dictionary and find five red words for each word class.

a verb

beg   _____ _____ _____ _____

b adjective

_____ _____ _____ _____ _____

c adverb

_____ _____ _____ _____ _____

d noun

_____ _____ _____ _____ _____

▶ **Exercise 38**

This concordance shows examples of the word *net* in use. Which are nouns, which are adjectives and which are verbs? Write the number of the line next to the correct word class.

a noun   _____

b adjective _1_____

c verb   _____

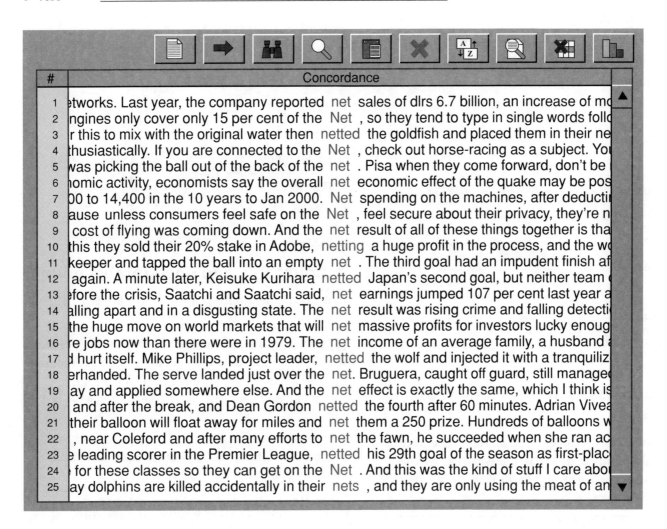

#	Concordance
1	etworks. Last year, the company reported net sales of dlrs 6.7 billion, an increase of mc
2	ngines only cover only 15 per cent of the Net , so they tend to type in single words follc
3	r this to mix with the original water then netted the goldfish and placed them in their ne
4	thusiastically. If you are connected to the Net , check out horse-racing as a subject. Yo
5	was picking the ball out of the back of the net . Pisa when they come forward, don't be
6	nomic activity, economists say the overall net economic effect of the quake may be pos
7	00 to 14,400 in the 10 years to Jan 2000. Net spending on the machines, after deducti
8	ause unless consumers feel safe on the Net , feel secure about their privacy, they're n
9	cost of flying was coming down. And the net result of all of these things together is tha
10	this they sold their 20% stake in Adobe, netting a huge profit in the process, and the wc
11	keeper and tapped the ball into an empty net . The third goal had an impudent finish af
12	again. A minute later, Keisuke Kurihara netted Japan's second goal, but neither team
13	efore the crisis, Saatchi and Saatchi said, net earnings jumped 107 per cent last year a
14	alling apart and in a disgusting state. The net result was rising crime and falling detecti
15	the huge move on world markets that will net massive profits for investors lucky enoug
16	re jobs now than there were in 1979. The net income of an average family, a husband
17	d hurt itself. Mike Phillips, project leader, netted the wolf and injected it with a tranquiliz
18	erhanded. The serve landed just over the net. Bruguera, caught off guard, still managec
19	ay and applied somewhere else. And the net effect is exactly the same, which I think is
20	and after the break, and Dean Gordon netted the fourth after 60 minutes. Adrian Vivea
21	their balloon will float away for miles and net them a 250 prize. Hundreds of balloons w
22	, near Coleford and after many efforts to net the fawn, he succeeded when she ran ac
23	e leading scorer in the Premier League, netted his 29th goal of the season as first-plac
24	for these classes so they can get on the Net . And this was the kind of stuff I care abo
25	ay dolphins are killed accidentally in their nets , and they are only using the meat of an

Interesting facts

The most common nouns in journalism are *year, time* and *years*. The most common nouns in business are *market, company* and *economy*.

2 Irregular noun plurals

Most nouns add -s for plural. Some add -es or -ies.
However there are some exceptions. The dictionary
shows these irregular noun plurals like this:

> **bookshelf** /ˈbʊkʃelf/ (plural **bookshelves** /ˈbʊkʃelvz/)
> noun [C] ★ a shelf that you put books on
> **bookshop** /ˈbʊkʃɒp/ noun [C] ★ a shop that sells

▶ **Exercise 39**

**Write the plural forms of the nouns below. Then check
your answers in the dictionary.**

singular form	plural form
a basis	*bases*
b hoof	
c half	
d analysis	
e tomato	
f cargo	
g volcano	
h crisis	
i chairman	
j phenomenon	

3 Nouns used in the singular or plural

Some nouns are used only in the singular, others are used
only in the plural, and some nouns when used in the
plural have a special meaning. The dictionary shows this
in the following way:

> week to telling them she was leaving.
> **build²** /bɪld/ noun (singular) ★ the size and shape of
> someone's body: *He was of medium build and about my
> height.*

> **glasses** /ˈglɑːsɪz/ noun (plural) ★ an object that you
> wear in front of your eyes to help you see better. You
> usually get your glasses from an **optician**: *Where are
> my glasses?* ♦ **wear glasses** *Most children hate having to*

> **3 minutes** (plural) an official written record of what is
> discussed or decided at a formal meeting: *Shall we hear
> the minutes of the last meeting?* ♦ **take the minutes** (=write
> them) *Carl usually takes the minutes but he's not here*

▶ **Exercise 40**

Tick the correct box for the nouns below.

	used only in the plural	has a special meaning when used in the plural
a flies	☐	☑
b manners	☐	☐
c thanks	☐	☐
d jeans	☐	☐
e scissors	☐	☐
f goods	☐	☐
g arms	☐	☐
h surroundings	☐	☐
i regards	☐	☐
j pyjamas	☐	☐

4 Countable and uncountable nouns

In the entries for nouns you will see the labels [C], [U] or
[C/U].

[C] means the noun is countable. It refers to single items
that can be counted and can be either singular or plural.

> **cat** /kæt/ noun [C] ★★★ an animal with soft fur, a long
> thin tail, and WHISKERS, that people keep as a pet or for

[U] means that the noun is uncountable. It refers to a
substance or quality which cannot be counted. It can't
usually follow the article *a* or *an*.

> **jewellery** /ˈdʒuːəlri/ noun [U] ★★ objects that you wear
> as decoration. Types of jewellery include **rings**, which

[C/U] can be either countable or uncountable. The more
frequent alternative is given first.

> **banana** /bəˈnɑːnə/ noun [C/U] ★ a long curved fruit
> with a yellow skin: *a bunch of bananas* — picture → C10

Note that some nouns can be either countable or
uncountable [C/U] depending on their meaning.

> **muscle¹** /ˈmʌsl/ noun ★★★
> **1** [C/U] a piece of flesh that connects one bone to
> another and is used for moving a particular part of
>
> **2** [U] physical strength: *It's going to take a lot of muscle
> to lift the fridge.* **2a.** the power that a person or organ-

▶ **Exercise 41**

Find these nouns in the dictionary. Put them in one or more of the three boxes below. Indicate the sense number where necessary.

improvement	luggage	encouragement	cigarette	advice
cloud	knowledge	paper	wine	experience

1 countable [C]	sense number
improvement	2

2 uncountable [U]	sense number

3 countable or uncountable [C/U]	sense number
improvement	1

5 Transitive and intransitive verbs

In the dictionary the symbol [T] indicates a verb that is followed by an object. The symbol [I] indicates a verb that isn't followed by an object or a complement and is not used in the passive. The dictionary shows this information in this way:

welcome[1] /'welkəm/ verb (T) ★★★ to greet someone in a polite and friendly way when they have come to see you or help you: *Some hotels do not even welcome*

occur /ə'kɜː/ verb (I) ★★★
1 to happen, especially unexpectedly: *Police said the accident occurred about 4.30 pm.* ♦ +**in** *Complications*

Many verbs can be both transitive and intransitive, sometimes with the same meaning, and sometimes with different meanings.

guess[1] /ges/ verb [I/T] ★★★ to say or decide what you think is true, without being certain about it: *a*

sound[2] /saʊnd/ verb ★★★
2 [I] to produce a sound: *The sirens sounded, warning of a tornado.* **2a.** [T] to make something produce a sound:
3 [T] to pronounce a particular letter in a word: PRONOUNCE: *He has trouble sounding the letter 'r'.* **3a.** to

▶ **Exercise 42**

Write down ten verbs that you yourself frequently use in English. Indicate if they are transitive [T] or intransitive [I] by ticking the correct column. Then check in the dictionary.

	[T]	[I]
_____	☐	☐
_____	☐	☐
_____	☐	☐
_____	☐	☐
_____	☐	☐
_____	☐	☐
_____	☐	☐
_____	☐	☐
_____	☐	☐
_____	☐	☐

6 Prepositions

Many verbs and adjectives are followed by a preposition. The dictionary tells you which prepositions to use in the following way:

> **long**⁴ /lɒŋ/ verb [I] ★ to want something very much: **(+for)** *It was freezing outside, and Marcia longed for a hot*

> **generous** /ˈdʒenərəs/ adj ★★
> *human being.* ♦ **(+to)** *Billy was very generous to people who had less than he did.* ♦ **(+with)** *Lawyers have been generous with their time and talents.* ♦ **generous of sb (to do sth)**

▶ **Exercise 43**

Complete the sentences with the correct prepositions. Check your answers in the dictionary.

a The children looked scared: they were clinging
   to _____ their mother.

b Rachel has never worried _____ finding a job.

c She wanted to prevent him _____ driving her car.

d They were always arguing _____ silly things.

e Please put out your cigarette. I object _____
   people smoking in the house.

f He succeeded _____ passing his exams, to my
   great surprise.

▶ **Exercise 44**

Choose the correct preposition from the box for each adjective. Then finish the sentences.

in	for	about	on	of	at	with	from

a You should be tolerant *of* ___ *other people's*
   opinion _____.

b I've always been interested _____ _____
   _____.

c I'm very fond _____ _____
   _____.

d My country is famous _____ _____
   _____.

e I'm very good _____ _____
   _____.

f If you work as a political correspondent, you need to be
   familiar _____ _____
   _____.

g I usually feel guilty _____ _____
   _____.

7 Verb patterns

Some verbs are followed by the infinitive form of the verb and some are followed by the -ing form of the verb. The dictionary shows this in the following way:

> **remember** /rɪˈmembə/ verb ★★★
> **1** [I/T] to have an image in your mind of a person, a place, or something that happened or was said in the past: *I can still remember every word of our conversation.* ♦ *That was a beautiful summer, as I remember.* ♦ **remember doing sth** *She remembers seeing him leave an hour ago.* ♦
> **(that)** *I remember*
> **3** [T] to do something that you promised to do, or that you have to do, and not forget about it: *I hope she remembers my book when she comes* (=remembers to bring it with her). ♦ **remember to do sth** *He never remembered to lock the door when he went out.*

▶ **Exercise 45**

Complete the sentences with the infinitive or the ...ing form of the verb in brackets. Check in the dictionary.

a If there is a mechanical problem, we suggest
   contacting (contact) the manufacturer directly.

b He's considering _____ (buy) a car.

c The committee decided unanimously _____
   (accept) the offer.

d I don't enjoy_____ (go) on holiday as much as
   I used to.

e I happened _____ (meet) an old friend in
   town.

f She closed her eyes and pretended _____ (be)
   asleep.

g They don't mind _____ (go) if no one else
   wants to.

h I expect _____ (get) paid on time.

i She had just finished _____ (dress) the
   children when the phone rang.

j I do think you should have offered _____
   (help).

8 Extra help in grammar boxes

Throughout the dictionary important grammatical information for common function words is given in grammar boxes at the beginning of the entries.

---

next /nekst/ function word ★★★

Next is used in the following ways:

as a **determiner** (followed by a noun): *I'll see you next week.*

as an **adjective**: *I'm leaving town on the next train. ♦ I didn't realize what had happened until the next day. ♦ I'm seeing him on Tuesday next.*

as a **pronoun**: *You're the next in line. ♦ I'll be seeing him the week after next.*

as an **adverb**: *What happens next? ♦ After me, he's the next tallest boy in the class.*

in the preposition phrase **next to**: *Come and sit next to me.*

Notice that:

1 this box is at the beginning of the entry;
2 this box summarizes the different uses of the word (i.e. determiner, adjective, pronoun and adverb);
3 examples are given.

▶ **Exercise 46**

Look at pages 1484–1495 in the dictionary. Notice how many of the words have boxes with additional grammatical information. List these words.

_____

_____

_____

_____

▶ **Exercise 47**

Read the sentences. Write the correct word class from the box next to each sentence according to the use of the underlined word. Check your answers in the dictionary.

| adverb | conjunction | determiner | pronoun |
| preposition | adjective | | |

a I've only been to Russia <u>once</u>.   *adverb*

b There's <u>no</u> answer. I'll ring again.   _____

c The marlin is <u>one</u> of the fastest animals in the world.   _____

d He's very honest <u>unlike</u> his brother.   _____

e <u>Though</u> I lived in Spain for a year, my Spanish is very poor.   _____

f Have we got <u>enough</u> for dinner for four?   _____

g Does <u>either</u> of you know how to get there?   _____

h He was standing on the <u>far</u> side of the room looking out.   _____

The dictionary also gives you more help on the grammar and meaning of some words in additional boxes at the end of the entry.

---

both /bəʊθ/ function word ★★★

Do not use **both** in negative sentences. Use **neither**: *Neither of my parents wanted me to leave school* (=my mother did not and my father did not).

Do not use **both...and...** in negative sentences. Use **neither...nor...**: *Mary neither drinks nor smokes.*

▶ **Exercise 48**

Use the grammar boxes in the dictionary to complete these sentences with one or more of the words.

a ago / before / for
  1 I arrived in London four weeks __*ago*__ .
  2 _____ that I'd been in France _____ a while.

b its / it's
  1 I've got a new cat. _____ called Ginger.
  2 My cat loves _____ food. I'm worried it's going to get too fat.

c few / a few
  1 Although _____ people made it to his party, he wasn't disappointed.
  2 Have you got _____ minutes to spare? I've got a problem.

d also / as well / too
  1 I suggest you ring them and send them an email _____ .
  2 Get some petrol and _____ check the oil.

e fewer / less
  1 I've got much _____ time to read these days.
  2 _____ books were sold this month than last.

Finding and exploring meanings

1 Finding the correct entry

Some words in the dictionary have more than one entry. That is because the same word can belong to different word classes. For example, the word *limit* can be either a verb or a noun, so there are two entries: limit¹, which is a verb, and limit², which is a noun. Notice the small numbers ¹ and ²: they tell you that there is more than one entry for the word.

> **limit¹** /ˈlɪmɪt/ verb [T] ★★★
> **1** to prevent a number, amount, or effect from increas-
>
> **limit²** /ˈlɪmɪt/ noun [C] ★★★
> **1** the greatest amount or level of something that is possible: **+to** *Obviously there is a limit to the amount we*

▶ **Exercise 49**

Look up the word *limp* in the dictionary and answer these questions.

a How many entries are there for the word *limp*?   _3_

b In which word classes is the word *limp* used?

   1 _____   2 _____   3 _____

c How many meanings are explained for the adjective *limp*?   _____

d Is the noun *limp* used in the plural?   _____

e Where do you find the adverb *limply*?   _____

f In which meaning of which entry for *limp* do you find the following examples:

   1 Rachel walks with a slight limp.   _____

   2 He was limping slightly and he looked tired.   _____

   3 a limp effort   _____

   4 The yacht is limping towards the island.   _____

   5 limp and lifeless hair   _____

Some words in English have the same spelling but two different meanings and pronunciations. These words are called *homographs*. The dictionary shows these in separate entries and the small numbers are used for these headwords too.

> **lead¹** /liːd/ (past tense and past participle **led** /led/) verb ★★★
>
> **lead²** /liːd/ noun ★★★
>
> **lead³** /led/ noun ★
> **1** [U] a soft heavy grey metal used especially in the

▶ **Exercise 50**

Circle the pairs of words that are pronounced differently in the sentences. Then write the pronunciation of each word. Check in your dictionary.

a (lead / lead)
   1 **Lead** is a type of metal.   _led_
   2 He was already in the **lead** after the first lap.   _liːd_

b mine / mine
   1 People still **mine** for gold in this area.   _____
   2 Is this your copy or **mine**?   _____

c read / read
   1 I must **read** his new book – everyone tells me it's excellent.   _____
   2 I only **read** ten books last year.   _____

d wind / wind
   1 The southerly **wind** brought moist air from the sea.   _____
   2 Don't forget to **wind** the clock up before you go to bed.   _____

e bear / bear

   1 I can't **bear** the thought of moving again.   _____

   2 A polar **bear** can run as fast as 40 kilometres per hour.   _____

f row / row

   1 I never saw him after our big **row**.   _____

   2 The best seats are in **row** five.   _____

g tears / tears

   1 She was so upset she burst into **tears**.   _____

   2 Watch the paper. It **tears** easily.   _____

2 Long entries

▶ Exercise 51

Look up the entry for *develop*. Notice the box at the beginning of the entry. How many meanings has this word got? _____

This box (called a menu) summarizes the definitions for the different meanings of the word. It helps you to find the meaning you are looking for quickly in a long entry. You can look at the numbered meanings below the menu if you want more information.

▶ Exercise 52

Look at the entry for *bounce¹* in the dictionary. Notice that there are six different meanings of the word shown in the menu and the entry below it. Match sentences a–f with meanings 1–6 in the menu. Write the correct number next to each letter.

a _3_   c _____   e _____

b _____   d _____   f _____

---

bounce¹ /baʊns/ verb ★★

1 hit surface	**5** when cheque is not paid
2 move up and down	**6** when email comes back
3 be reflected	**+** PHRASES
4 move energetically	

---

a Sonar detects distance and depth by sound waves bouncing off an object.

b My bank charged £30 for the cheque that bounced?

c I've got your email address wrong. My emails keep bouncing.

d He came bouncing into the room.

e The jeep bounced along the rough country road.

f The ball bounced off the crossbar into the goal.

▶ Exercise 53

Read through the entry for *bounce¹* again. Using the example sentences and the definitions, make a list of some of the things that can bounce.

   ball _____ _____

_____ _____ _____

It isn't always easy to find the information you are looking for if an entry has a lot of meanings. The menu will help you, so look there first to see if you can find a definition that fits the meaning you want.

▶ Exercise 54

Look at the entry for the verb *run* and answer these questions.

a How many meanings are explained?   _____

b Write the number of the meaning that:

   1 explains *run* used with machines   _____

   2 refers to electing a politician   _____

   3 refers to something illegal   _____

   4 refers to travel   _____

▶ Exercise 55

Look at meaning 6 of the verb *run* and answer the questions. Notice that there are three definitions here: 6, 6a and 6b.

a Which vehicles are mentioned in the definition for meaning 6?

   _____

b How many examples are there?   _____

c How late was the train?   _____

d Where do you find this example: *John kindly offered to run me into town.*   _____

e In which of the meanings is the driver not controlling a vehicle properly?   _____

f What did the truck run into?   _____

▶ **Exercise 56**

Common words with several meanings

Most of the clues in this crossword are taken from the menus at the beginning of the entry. These show that the word has several meanings.

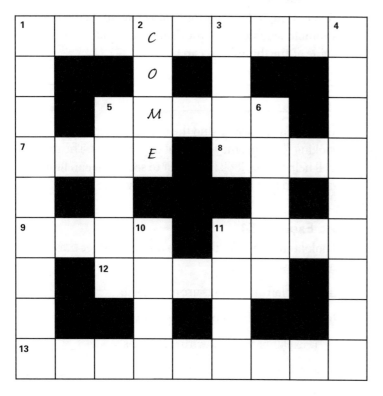

DOWN

1

1 qualities of personality	5 unusual person
2 what makes sth different	6 ...
3 sb's reputation	7 ...
4 sb in book, film etc	

2

1 move/travel (to here)	6 ...
2 [+ to] reach particular state	7 ...
3 [+ into] start doing sth	8 ...
4 reach particular point	9 ...
5 be received	+ PHRASES

3

1 move while turning	6 wrap sth around itself
2 move on wheels	7 ...
3 move from side to side	8 ...
4 change direction faced	9 ...
5 move across surface	+ PHRASES

4

1 way sth is moving/facing	5 control/management
2 instructions	6 ...
3 way sb/sth changes	7 ...
4 purpose	+ PHRASES

5 (plural)

1 small piece of paper	5 in cricket
2 slight mistake	6 ...
3 sliding/falling	+ PHRASES
4 piece of clothing	

6

1 bright/well lit/not dark	7 ...
2 pale in colour	8 ...
3 not weighing much	9 ...
4 small/not much	10 ...
5 not severe	+ PHRASES
6 ...	

10

Something that you wear on each foot, usually over socks.

11

1 sth you can sit on	4 clothing covering bottom
2 place on committee etc	5 position on horse
3 main place/building	+ PHRASES

ACROSS

1

1 worried	4 giving your attention
2 involved/affected	5 ...
3 feeling care for sb	+ PHRASES

5

1 not large in size/amount	5 about letters
2 not important/difficult	6 voice/sound: quiet
3 not worth much money	+ PHRASES
4 children: very young	

7

1 govern country/area	4 be the most important
2 make decision	5 draw straight line
3 influence thought/action	+ PHRASES

8

1 have home in place	5 continue to exist
2 have kind of life	6 have interesting life
3 keep alive certain way	7 ...
4 be/stay alive	+ PHRASES

9 (plural)

1 soft hat	6 ...
2 lid/covering	7 ...
3 limit on money	8 ...
4 top part	+ PHRASES
5 artificial tooth cover	

11

1 when gun is fired	6 ...
2 throw/hit/kick of ball	7 ...
3 view/photograph	8 ...
4 attempt to do/get sth	9 ...
5 sth said/done as attack	+ PHRASES

12

A large piece of thin cloth that you put on your bed and use for lying on or covering your body when you sleep.

13

1 where visitors are met	4 quality of picture/sound
2 formal party	5 ...
3 ...	+ PHRASES

▶ **Exercise 57**

Common words with several meanings

Most of the clues in this crossword are taken from the menus at the beginning of the entry. These show that the word has several meanings.

```
¹R E ²S U ³L T   [ ] ⁴[ ] ⁵[ ]  ⁶[ ]  ⁷[ ]
```

(crossword grid with numbered cells 1–26)

ACROSS

1

1 sth caused by sth else	5 ...
2 score/name of winner	6 ...
3 information obtained	7 ...
4 mark in examination	

4

1 relaxed and satisfied	4 flavour: smooth/full
2 colours: soft and warm	5 gentle and wise
3 sound: smooth/pleasant	

8

1 where two sides meet	5 difficult situation
2 bend/meeting of roads	6 in football/hockey etc
3 end of mouth/eye	7 in boxing/wrestling
4 small (quiet) area	+ PHRASES

10

1 try hard to do sth	4 separate solid & liquid
2 make relationship bad	5 pull/push sth hard
3 injure muscle	+ PHRASES

11 (past tense)

1 arrive/bring	4 be in bad situation
2 come down to ground	5 catch fish
3 get sth you wanted	+ PHRASES

12

1 body part for seeing	5 hole in needle
2 expression on sb's face	6 ...
3 for saying sb is looking	7 ...
4 calm centre of storm	+ PHRASES

13

1 continue in space/time	5 lend money etc
2 increase size/range etc	6 affect/include sth/sb
3 increase length	+ PHRASES
4 offer greeting	

16

1 frequent/frequently	4 reaching usual standard
2 used/done etc by group	5 of low social class
3 ordinary	+ PHRASES

20

1 liquid for fuel	4 for your skin
2 used in engines	5 type of paint
3 used in cooking	+ PHRASES

21

1 person: kind and calm	4 slope/shape: gradual
2 movement: lacking force	5 heat: low
3 wind/rain: not strong	

22

Makes someone feel sad, worried, or angry.

23

1 get away from sth bad	4 come out by accident
2 avoid sth unpleasant	5 go away on holiday
3 not remember/notice	+ PHRASES

25 (past tense)

1 for agreement	4 in football
2 for pointing/signalling	5 move slightly
3 as greeting etc	+ PHRASES

26

The things you can gain or lose by taking a risk, for example in business or politics.

DOWN

1

1 beautifully/expensively	4 with a lot of money etc
2 strongly and attractively	5 to great degree
3 completely	

2

1 thin rope	6 ...
2 group/series of things	7 ...
3 on instrument	8 ...
4 on tennis racket etc	+ PHRASES
5 sth like string	

3

1 be/put yourself flat	5 be in particular state
2 be in place/on surface	6 ...
3 in a competition	7 ...
4 consist of	+ PHRASES

5

1 area of buildings	4 rulers of country
2 of dead person	5 situation or state
3 large car	

6

1 carrying a load	5 very rich
2 very full	6 ...
3 containing bullets	+ PHRASES
4 with second meaning	

7

1 travel without purpose	4 look at something else
2 move away from place	5 talk about sth else
3 stop concentrating	6 when path/river curves

9

1 improve sth	4 pay back money
2 receive value of shares	5 save sb from evil
3 use voucher	+ PHRASES

14

1 organ in mouth	4 ...
2 language	5 long narrow piece
3 way of speaking/writing	+ PHRASES

15

1 tall thick post	4 of writing/numbers
2 sth rising into the air	5 in newspaper/magazine
3 line of people/vehicles	

16

1 covering passage/hole	5 with fixed number of sth
2 not doing business	6 forming complete circle
3 not allowed to everyone	+ PHRASES
4 not considering ideas	

17

1 authority/responsibility	4 piece of clothing
2 sth that covers/hides	5 part of the Earth
3 cover for flame	

18

1 use violence to harm	4 begin with enthusiasm
2 strongly criticize	5 try to score points
3 cause damage/disease	

19 (plural)

1 amount	5 ...
2 standard/status	6 ...
3 part/stage of system	7 ...
4 floor in building	+ PHRASES

24

1 group of things	7 ...
2 group of people	8 ...
3 piece of equipment	9 ...
4 stage/scenery	10 ...
5 part of tennis match	11 ...
6 way sb stand/sits/looks	

3 Understanding definitions

The dictionary gives you the meaning of words in short and clear definitions that use a carefully selected defining vocabulary of 2500 words. (This is given on pages 1677–1689 of the dictionary). Any word in a definition that is not one of the 2500 words appears in small capital letters. You can find the meaning of these words elsewhere in the dictionary.

All the words in this definition are within the 2500 defining vocabulary.

palace /ˈpæləs/ noun [C] ★★
1 a very large building, especially one used as the official home of a royal family, president, or important religious leader: *the presidential palace* **1a.** **Palace** used

The word *printing press* is not within the 2500 defining vocabulary but its meaning can be found in the dictionary.

print¹ /prɪnt/ verb ★★★
1 [I/T] to produce words, numbers, pictures etc on paper, using a printer or PRINTING PRESS: *I had already printed twenty pages when I noticed the page numbers were*

▶ **Exercise 58**

Match the example sentences (a–f) to the definitions (1–6). What is common about these words and phrases? Write the missing word on the line at the end.

a I'm not sure how much of his explanation she <u>took in</u>.

b Everyone laughed, but Harold didn't seem to <u>get</u> the joke.

c I couldn't <u>follow</u> what Professor Hope was saying.

d There was a pause while she <u>digested</u> this piece of news.

e We had to <u>figure out</u> the connection between the two events.

f How could you possibly <u>comprehend</u> the difficulties of my situation?

1 to _____ something, especially something long and complicated

2 to be able to _____ something or solve a problem

3 to _____ and remember something that you hear or read

4 to _____ someone or something (informal)

5 to _____ something (formal)

6 to _____ information when there is a lot of it or it is difficult or unexpected

Missing word: _____

▶ **Exercise 59**

1 Look at the four groups of words. What is common about all of them?

a	b	c	d
duck	bird of paradise	emu	hummingbird
falcon	jay	kiwi	peacock
flamingo	puffin	condor	sparrow
kingfisher	dodo	penguin	canary
swan	heron	ostrich	lark

2 Circle the odd one out in each column. Explain your choice.

a _____

b _____

c _____

d _____

3 Check the definitions in the dictionary to see if your answers are correct.

▶ **Exercise 60**

Read the dictionary definitions and choose the word that each describes. Check your answers in the dictionary.

1 To walk slowly and noisily without lifting your feet.

   a limp b hobble ⓒshuffle

2 A wooden house built in a mountain area, especially in Switzerland. Its roof usually has steep sides.

   a chalet b dacha c chateau

3 The last few words of a joke, including the part that makes the joke funny.

   a punch line b main line c chorus line

4 A doctor whose job is to check the health of a woman who is pregnant and help with the birth of her child.

   a obstetrician b dermatologist c paediatrician

5 A person whose attention is fixed on only one thing can be called:

   a simple-minded b narrow-minded

   c single-minded

6 To go somewhere very quickly because you are angry or upset.

   a burst out b storm out c step out

4 Examples

The examples in the dictionary show you how a word or phrase is used in real contexts. The example phrases and sentences appear in italics and they are divided by the ♦ symbol. Remember to read the examples – they give you additional information and understanding about the use of the word.

funny /ˈfʌni/ adj ★★★
1 someone or something that is funny makes you laugh: *a funny story / joke* ♦ *one of Britain's funniest comedians* ♦ *I don't think that's at all funny.* ♦ *Wouldn't it be funny if we played a trick on him?* **1a.** it's/that's/this

5 Checking what you know

▶ **Exercise 61**

1 Write down three English words that you know and use.

   _____ _____ _____

2 Look up each word and notice:

   a how many meanings it has
   b if it is a red word and how many stars it has
   c the examples
   d the pronunciation and stress
   e anything else

3 Have you learnt anything new about this word and how to use it?

   _____

   _____

▶ **Exercise 62**

1 Write down three English words whose meaning you are uncertain of.

   _____ _____ _____

2 Look up each word and notice:

   a if it is a frequent word
   b how many meanings it has
   c which meaning is the most frequent
   d how the word is used in the example(s)
   e the pronunciation and stress
   f anything else

3 Do you feel ready to use this word?

   _____

▶ **Exercise 63**

Here is a concordance showing real examples of a single word in use. This word
has been removed from the sentences.

1 Read the sentences. Can you guess the missing word? _____

2 Look up this word in the dictionary, and match its different meanings with
  the examples below. Write the correct headword number next to each
  sentence.

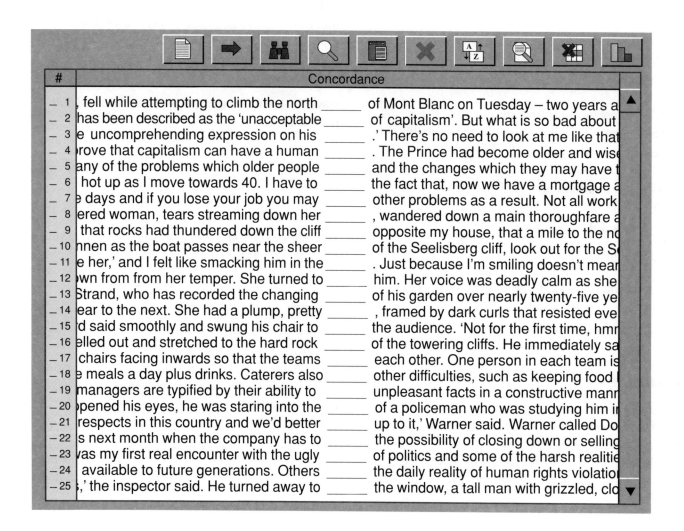

#	Concordance
— 1	, fell while attempting to climb the north _____ of Mont Blanc on Tuesday – two years a
— 2	has been described as the 'unacceptable _____ of capitalism'. But what is so bad about
— 3	e uncomprehending expression on his _____ .' There's no need to look at me like that
— 4	rove that capitalism can have a human _____ . The Prince had become older and wise
— 5	any of the problems which older people _____ and the changes which they may have t
— 6	hot up as I move towards 40. I have to _____ the fact that, now we have a mortgage a
— 7	e days and if you lose your job you may _____ other problems as a result. Not all work
— 8	ered woman, tears streaming down her _____ , wandered down a main thoroughfare a
— 9	that rocks had thundered down the cliff _____ opposite my house, that a mile to the nc
— 10	nnen as the boat passes near the sheer _____ of the Seelisberg cliff, look out for the S
— 11	e her,' and I felt like smacking him in the _____ . Just because I'm smiling doesn't mear
— 12	wn from her temper. She turned to _____ him. Her voice was deadly calm as she
— 13	Strand, who has recorded the changing _____ of his garden over nearly twenty-five ye
— 14	ear to the next. She had a plump, pretty _____ , framed by dark curls that resisted eve
— 15	d said smoothly and swung his chair to _____ the audience. 'Not for the first time, hmr
— 16	elled out and stretched to the hard rock _____ of the towering cliffs. He immediately sa
— 17	chairs facing inwards so that the teams _____ each other. One person in each team is
— 18	e meals a day plus drinks. Caterers also _____ other difficulties, such as keeping food l
— 19	managers are typified by their ability to _____ unpleasant facts in a constructive mann
— 20	pened his eyes, he was staring into the _____ of a policeman who was studying him ir
— 21	respects in this country and we'd better _____ up to it,' Warner said. Warner called Do
— 22	s next month when the company has to _____ the possibility of closing down or selling
— 23	vas my first real encounter with the ugly _____ of politics and some of the harsh realitie
— 24	available to future generations. Others _____ the daily reality of human rights violatio
— 25	,' the inspector said. He turned away to _____ the window, a tall man with grizzled, clc

Interesting facts

The most common nouns in conversation are *time*,
people and *thing*. The most common nouns in
non-fiction and fiction are *time*, *people* and *way*.

▶ **Exercise 64**

Easy crossword

Most of the clues in this crossword contain a word in red. If you want help, look up this word in the dictionary.

| 1 D | 2 E | | A | L | | 3 | 4 | | 5 | | 6 | | 7 |

(crossword grid)

ACROSS

1   At the beginning of a card game, you shuffle the cards and then _____ them to the players. (4)

3   A hard situation is one that is unpleasant and full of _____ . (8)

9   Myths are ancient traditional _____ . (7)

10 A leek is a type of vegetable that tastes similar to an _____ . (5)

11 Cod live in the Atlantic _____ . (5)

12 A stadium is generally used for sports _____ . (6)

14 A word that is used for emphasizing that you mean all or every part of something. (6)

16 A pinprick is the quick pain that you feel when a _____ is pushed into your skin. (6)

19 A baby's toy that makes a noise when it is shaken. (6)

21 Ice hockey is played by two _____ of six players. (5)

24 If a flower comes out, it _____ . (5)

25 Christmas Eve is the _____ before Christmas Day. (7)

26 A live radio programme can be _____ to at the same time as it happens. (8)

27 _____ live in hives and make honey. (4)

DOWN

1   If you are the first person to find, see, or understand something, you _____ it. If it already exists, you cannot say that you've invented it. (8)

2   If you are unaccompanied when you go somewhere, you go _____ . (5)

4   If you feel refreshed, you are more lively and comfortable because you have _____ , washed and eaten. (6)

5   'She slipped and _____ her arm.' (5)

6   If something has never happened or _____ before, it is unprecedented. (7)

7   A verse is one section of a poem or _____ . (4)

8   To dine is to eat _____ . (6)

13 Nerves are the fibres that carry _____ between your brain and the rest of your body. (8)

15 You turn the steering wheel to control the direction a vehicle _____ in. (7)

17 You can push a swing door open from _____ side. (6)

18 If you get tough with someone, you decide to deal with them in a very _____ way. (6)

20 A flavoured drink has had something added to give it a particular _____ . (5)

22 An object is a thing that is not _____ . (5)

23 Hamburgers are usually eaten in a bread _____ . (4)

xx# 32

Exploring a dictionary page

▶ **Exercise 65**

Find the answers to the questions in the information on this dictionary page.

xxxx

cosmonaut   313

correspondent

2 someone who regularly writes letters or emails to another person

correspondent² /ˌkɒrɪˈspɒndənt/ adj formal suitable for a particular situation

corresponding /ˌkɒrɪˈspɒndɪŋ/ adj [only before noun] ★★
1 related to or connected with something: *Investment in the railways will bring a corresponding improvement in services.* ♦ **corresponding increase / decrease / decline / fall** *Rising prosperity has not been matched by any corresponding decrease in crime.*
2 similar to or the same as something: EQUIVALENT: *Income from tourism is five per cent higher than in the corresponding period last year.* ♦ *Nurses smoke as much as corresponding groups in the general population.*

correspondingly /ˌkɒrɪˈspɒndɪŋli/ adv used for saying that one thing is related to another, or is caused by another: *The service is better and correspondingly more expensive.*

corridor /ˈkɒrɪdɔː/ noun [C] ★★
1 a long passage inside a building with doors on each side: *a hotel / hospital corridor* ♦ *I went along the corridor to her office.* **1a.** a passage on a train
2 a long narrow area of land that people or animals travel through: *A natural corridor at the foot of the Alps.* ♦ *wildlife corridors* **2a.** used about an area of land that belongs to one country but is surrounded by another **2b.** used about the land near a major river, road, or railway line: *the east Thames corridor*

the corridors (of power) *mainly journalism* the places where people use their political influence and major political decisions are made: *the lobbyists who inhabit the corridors of power in Washington*

corroborate /kəˈrɒbəreɪt/ verb [T] formal to support what someone says by giving information or evidence that agrees with them: BEAR OUT: *Details of the killings were corroborated by official documents.*

corroboration /kəˌrɒbəˈreɪʃn/ noun [U] formal evidence or information that supports what someone has said

corroborative /kəˈrɒb(ə)rətɪv/ adj formal corroborative evidence supports what someone has said

corroboree /kəˈrɒbəri/ noun [C] Australian an ABORIGINAL festival of singing and dancing

corrode /kəˈrəʊd/ verb **1** [I/T] if metal or another substance corrodes, or if something corrodes it, it is gradually destroyed by a chemical reaction: *Acid rain poisons fish, destroys forests, and corrodes buildings.* ♦ *The metal structure is corroding badly and needs to be replaced.*
2 [T] formal to make something weak by causing gradual damage: *a society corroded by fear*

corrosion /kəˈrəʊʒn/ noun [U] damage caused to metal or stone when it is corroded: *corrosion-resistant metals*

bank was closed down amid allegations of corruption and fraud. ♦ *the arrest of a number of officials on corruption charges*
2 the process of CORRUPTING someone or something: *corruption of the morals of the young* ♦ *corruption of the database*
3 literary the process of decay, especially in a dead body

corsage /kɔːˈsɑːʒ/ noun [C] a decoration made of flowers that a woman wears on a dress or suit

corsair /ˈkɔːseə/ noun [C] an old word for a 'pirate'

corset /ˈkɔːsɪt/ noun [C] **1** a stiff piece of underwear worn by women to make their waists look thin, especially in the past **1a.** a piece of clothing that looks like a corset **2** medical a piece of clothing designed to support your back

corseted /ˈkɔːsɪtɪd/ adj wearing a corset

cortège /kɔːˈteɪʒ/ noun [C] a line of people and cars taking part in a funeral

cortex /ˈkɔːteks/ (plural **cortices** /ˈkɔːtɪsiːz/) noun [C] medical the outer layer of your brain or another organ: *the cerebral cortex*

cortisone /ˈkɔːtɪzəʊn/ noun [U] a drug that is an artificial HORMONE, used to improve medical conditions such as ARTHRITIS and ALLERGIES

coruscating /ˈkɒrəˌskeɪtɪŋ/ adj very formal lively and impressive: *a coruscating performance*

corvette /kɔːˈvet/ noun [C] a small fast ship that is used for protecting other ships

cos¹ /kəz/ conjunction Br E informal a way of writing 'because' that shows how it sounds in informal speech: *You'll have to pay, cos I've got no money.*

cos² abbrev cosine

Cosa Nostra, the /ˌkəʊzə ˈnɒstrə/ the MAFIA

COSATU /kəˈsɑːtuː/ Congress of South African Trade Unions: a large and powerful organization in South Africa that represents many different TRADE UNIONS

cosh¹ /kɒʃ/ noun [C] Br E informal a weapon shaped like a short thick stick
under the cosh Br E informal experiencing difficulty or criticism: *The home team was soon under the cosh.*

cosh² /kɒʃ/ verb [T] Br E informal to hit someone with a cosh

cosign /ˈkəʊsaɪn/ verb [T] to sign a cheque, contract, formal agreement etc together with another person

cosine /ˈkəʊsaɪn/ noun [C] in a RIGHT-ANGLED TRIANGLE, the measurement of an ACUTE angle that is equal to the length of the side between the angle and the right angle divided by the length of the HYPOTENUSE

cos lettuce /ˌkɒs ˈletɪs/ noun [C/U] Br E a type of long thin LETTUCE

---

a Which of these words is more frequent in English?
 1 *correspondent²* 2 *corresponding*

b Which words have both a primary and a secondary stress?

_____

_____

_____

c What is *cos¹* an abbreviation for? _____

d How many red words are there on this page? _____

e List four nouns *corresponding* often occurs with.

_____

f What is the plural form of the noun *cortex*? _____

▶ **Exercise 66**

Look up page 311 in the dictionary. Study the page and see how quickly you can find the answers to these questions.

a Which syllable has the primary stress in these words?

1 *corollary* _____

2 *corona* _____

3 *coronary* _____

4 *coroner* _____

b What is a word for a small crown?

_____

c What is the pronunciation of these words?

1 *corps* (singular) _____

2 *corps* (plural) _____

d What is the ceremony at which someone becomes king or queen?

_____

e Which nouns are frequently used with the word *corporate*?

_____

_____

_____

f Can the adjective *corporate* follow a noun?

_____

g What word can refer to both a musical instrument and an ice cream?

_____

h What are cornflakes made from?

_____

i What are two words with different spellings and meanings that have the pronunciation /ˈkɔːnˌflaʊə/

_____   _____

j What four compound nouns begin with *corporate*?

_____

_____

_____

_____

k In what subject areas are these compound nouns used?

_____

l What is the name of a small typically English meat pie?

_____

m What use of the word *corn* can refer to a hairstyle?

_____

n Which two words have the same spelling and pronunciation and can be used as a noun and an adjective?

_____

_____

o Find a word on the page that is labelled:

1 British English _____

2 American English _____

3 formal _____

4 very formal _____

5 old-fashioned _____

6 literary _____

7 technical _____

8 science _____

9 medical _____

10 business _____

Collocations, idioms and phrasal verbs

1 Collocations

When learning English words, it is useful to learn the words they often occur with (their collocations). The dictionary helps you to know which words are frequently used together. One way in which information is given on collocations is in a box at the end of the entry. Notice the small number in the box. This tells you which meaning of the word is used with these words.

Words frequently used with **join**		
nouns	army, band, club, group, party, team, union	**1**

▶ **Exercise 67**

Read the questions and circle the correct words. Check your answers in the dictionary.

a Which adverbs do you think are frequently used with the word *possible*?

fairly   rather   (perfectly)   (entirely)   (quite)   (always)

b Which adjectives do you think are most frequently used with the word *sense* (= the meaning of a word or phrase)?

usual   wide   strict   normal   literal   broad

c Which verbs do you think frequently occur with the word *sense* (=feeling)?

convey   create   tell   develop   make   see

d Which nouns do you think frequently go with the word *negotiate*?

contract   arrangement   price   work   deal

▶ **Exercise 68**

List three words that you think typically occur with these words. Check in the dictionary.

a verb
1 *turn* _____ _____ _____ head

2 _____ _____ _____ payment

b adjectives
1 _____ _____ _____ leg

2 _____ _____ _____ contribution

c adverbs
1 listen   _____ _____ _____

2 reduce   _____ _____ _____

d nouns
1 popular _____ _____ _____

2 brief   _____ _____ _____

▶ **Exercise 69**

Look at the extract of the entry for the word *easy*[1]. In this part of the entry you can see typical collocations formed with the word. These are shown like this:

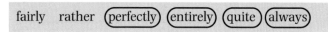

easy[1] /ˈiːzi/ adj ★★★
1 not difficult to do, or not needing much work: *Finding somewhere to live in London isn't easy.* ♦ **easy to do** *This cake is very easy to make.* ♦ *It's quite an easy game to learn.* ♦ **it is easy to do sth** *It is not always easy to find good teaching materials in this field.* ♦ (quite / fairly / relatively) easy *I'll show you how to work the till – it's quite easy.* ♦ **an easy way to do sth** *The easiest way to get to Hertford is on the train.* ♦ **make sth easy** *We all thought computers would make our jobs easier.* **1a.** not difficult to know, understand, or believe: *Here's an easy question to start with.* ♦ **easy to do** *His explanations are clear and easy to follow.* ♦ **it is easy to see** *It is easy to see why she likes him.*

The meaning of these collocations is clear and can be guessed from the individual words, i.e. they are not idiomatic.

2 Idioms and phrases

English contains many idiomatic expressions.

1 An idiomatic expression is a combination of words with a particular meaning.
2 The meaning cannot usually be guessed from the individual words.
3 Words cannot usually be left out or put in a different order, so words, word order and meaning need to be learnt as a whole. The dictionary helps you by giving the word order, meaning and usage of idiomatic expressions.

> **let your hair down** *informal* to relax and enjoy yourself because you are in a comfortable environment

> **shake like a leaf** to shake a lot, for example because you are cold, nervous, or afraid: *Put on a sweater – you're shaking like a leaf!*

▶ **Exercise 70**

Complete the idioms with a word from the box. Check in your dictionary.

prey wisdom chance mind bearings pocket spot press inch matter corner mile

a not give an *inch*

b to bear in _____

c to fall _____ to something

d no laughing _____

e to find your _____

f hot off the _____

g a sore _____

h words of _____

i turn a _____

j on the off _____

k stand out a _____

l pick someone's _____

3 Finding an idiom and phrase

To find an idiom or phrase in the dictionary, try following these steps:

1 Decide which is the keyword in the idiomatic expression. Usually this word is a noun or verb, sometimes an adjective or adverb.
2 Look up the keyword in the dictionary to see if the idiom is there. If not, try one of the other words.
3 Idioms are given after the definitions of the different senses of the word.

> **hit the roof/ceiling** *spoken* to become very angry

> **have your hands full** to be extremely busy with a difficult job

▶ **Exercise 71**

1 Read the sentences and underline the idiomatic expression in each.
2 Guess the keyword in the idiom and look up this word to find the meaning of the idiom.

keyword

a She has always been the <u>apple of her father's eye</u>.   *apple*

b At the last meeting I got cold feet and I haven't been since. _____

c It's been difficult but now there is light at the end of the tunnel. _____

d It seems pretty risky, but I think we'll take the plunge. _____

e He's not in her good books. _____

f It's obvious what you have to do: here it is in black and white. _____

▶ **Exercise 72**

Colourful crossword

Most of the clues and words in this crossword are connected with colours.

Grid (5 Across filled in): C A U G H T

ACROSS

5 If someone sees you doing something wrong, you have been _____ red-handed. (6)

6 The buying and selling of company shares before they are officially available is known as the grey _____ . (6)

8 If you write in a very emotional or complicated style, you are writing purple _____ . (5)

9 Somebody who is blue-blooded comes from a family of a very high social _____ . (5)

11 Blue-collar workers do work that involves using physical strength or _____ with their hands. (5)

13 To do or say something that you know will harm someone's reputation is to blacken their _____ . (9)

16 Titanium is an expensive white metal named after this kind of giant. (5)

18 A clear slightly brown jelly that you put fish or meat into and allow to become cold before eating. (5)

19 The name of a green place in a desert where there is water and where plants and trees grow. (5)

20 A blue-chip company makes a lot of money and is safe to _____ in. (6)

21 A very happy or exciting day is a red-_____ day. (6)

DOWN

1 If your relations do not approve of you because they think you behave badly, you are the black sheep of the _____ . (6)

2 If you are 'beyond the black stump', you are certainly a long way from any _____ . (5) (Australian English)

3 Providing services in the black economy allows you to avoid paying any _____ . (5)

4 When someone criticizes another person for a fault that they also have, we say that this is 'the pot calling the _____ black'. (6)

7 A red flag is used as the sign of _____ . (9)

10 The name of the most common vowel sound in the English language, a 'colourless' vowel found only in unstressed syllables and represented by the symbol /ə/. (5)

12 When you are frightened, this part of your body is said to knock. (5)

14 'Every cloud has a silver _____' is used to say that something good usually comes out of a bad situation. (6)

15 A woman who only wants relationships with rich men is called a gold _____ . (6)

17 A radio or television that is not receiving the correct signal makes white _____ . (5)

18 Very pale, especially because you feel ill or upset. Also the colour of the powder that remains after something has burned. (5)

4 Phrasal verbs

All the common English verbs (e.g. *take*, *look*, *come*) can combine with prepositions and adverbs (often called particles) to make phrasal verbs. The dictionary shows phrasal verbs with their definitions and examples at the end of the main entry for the verb.

,run a'way with phrasal vb [T] **1** [**run away with sb**] to secretly leave a place with someone so that you can live together: *She ran away with her teacher when she was only sixteen.* **2** [**run away with sb**] if feelings, ideas etc run away with someone, they make someone say or do something stupid **3** [**run away with sth**] to steal something, or borrow something without asking **4** [**run away with sth**] *informal* to win a competition, game, or prize very easily

,run 'into phrasal vb [T] **1** [**run into sb**] to meet someone when you did not expect to: *Guess who I ran into this morning?* **2** [**run into sb/sth**] to hit someone or something by accident while you are driving: *A truck ran into me* (=hit my car) *at the lights this morning.*

▶ **Exercise 73**

Look at the verbs in the sentences. Circle the particle that fits the meaning. Check in the dictionary.

a The plane took (off) / over / up later than expected.
b These little scooters have suddenly caught off / on / out.
c We were a little put in / off / out when our guests suddenly cancelled their visit.
d We shouldn't read too much into / onto / out the director's statement.
e I ran at / into / up my English teacher in the town centre.
f At first everyone was taken in / off / out by the explanations.

▶ **Exercise 74**

Complete the sentences with the correct particles. Use your dictionary to check your answers.

a The teacher took __apart__ everything the student had written.
b As a youngster I looked up _____ my sports heroes.
c He takes _____ his mother.
d He's looked _____ by his grandmother during the week.

e Thanks, I may take you up _____ your offer of a lift.
f He had a tendency to look down _____ people who left a lot of litter.
g She's too upset – she'll never take him _____ .

▶ **Exercise 75**

Choose a verb and one or two particles from the boxes and write true sentences.

get	put	come	bring	turn

on	along	behind	up	away	out	across	into

a *I get on well with my parents most of the time.*
b _____
c _____
d _____
e _____
f _____

If you would like to learn more about phrasal verbs, turn to page LA3 in your dictionary.

▶ **Exercise 76**

Phrasal verbs and phrases

This crossword contains phrasal verbs and phrases. The main verb in the answer is given in jumbled order. You have to provide the adverbs and prepositions as necessary.

The grid shows 7 ACROSS filled in as: **F I G U R E**

ACROSS

7 When you solve a problem or try hard to understand a situation, you _____ it out. (6) (geirfu)

8 When you stop trying to help or change somebody, and stop hoping that they will improve, you _____ them. (4,2,2) (iveg)

9 Someone who has finished smoking a cigarette normally _____ it _____ in an ashtray. (5,3) (usbts)

10 Someone who is washing their hair puts shampoo through it, and then _____ it out again. (6) (iesrsn)

11 If you do someone else's work while they are away or ill, you _____ them. (5,3) (cervo)

12 If you cut something off something else in one smooth movement, you _____ it _____ . (3,3) (olp)

13 If someone suddenly says something surprising or shocking, we say that they _____ it. (4,3,4) (moce)

18 A phrase which can mean 'succeed', and 'manage to come'. (4,2) (eakm)

20 To give knowledge or skill to someone who is younger than you and will live after you have died. (4,4) (dnah)

22 To make a short visit somewhere. (4,2) (opdr)

23 A pond that has become covered with ice is _____ . (4,4) (ceid)

24 When you take action to solve a problem, you _____ the problem. (4,4) (aedl)

25 If you are in London, and you are talking to a person who lives in London, that person might say, 'I've _____ to Scotland twice this year.' (4,2) (eenb)

DOWN

1 A phrase meaning 'continues to diet'. (5,2) (iedts)

2 When you realize or understand something, you _____ it. (6,2) (melbut)

3 If you have done something wrong for which you should be punished, the person in authority (such as your teacher or the police) can decide whether to punish you or to _____ you _____ . (3,3) (elt)

4 A place is said to _____ with people when there are too many people to fit in. (8) (lwofevro)

5 A thing that is found by accident after it has been lost is said to _____ . (4,2) (ntur)

6 If a door handle isn't attached very well, and you pull it too hard, it might _____ . (4,3) (omec)

8 If you plan to do something, then you are not sure that you want to, and then you do it anyway, you _____ it. (2,7,4) (og)

14 If you are having dinner at home instead of going out to a restaurant, you are _____ . (6,2) (teagni)

15 If a friend has no money but will get some soon, you might lend them some money in order to _____ them _____ until their money arrives. (4,4) (dite)

16 If you become so excited or involved in something that you lose control of your feelings, you get _____ away. (7) (rciaedr)

17 When you _____ , you use a broom to remove the dirt from the floor. (5,2) (eweps)

19 Forces someone out of a foreign country. (6) (lxpsee)

21 When you want to say that you'll do something if it's necessary, you may say 'I'll do it if _____ .' (4,2) (eb)

► **Exercise 77**

Phrasal verbs and phrases

The clues and answers in this crossword all contain phrasal verbs and phrases.

(crossword grid with answer 3 across filled as T A K I N G)

DOWN

1 To criticize someone, especially when other people are present, in a way that makes them feel stupid. (3,4)
2 To take care of someone or something and make certain that they have everything they need. (4,5)
3 To put on a piece of clothing in order to see how it looks and whether it fits. (3,2)
4 A unit for measuring length. Also used as a verb with *along* to mean 'move very slowly and gradually'. (4)
5 To increase in price. (2,2)
8 To give your time to something and make progress with it. Also, to like each other and be friendly to each other. (3,2,4)
11 If you _____ with someone's suggestion, you agree with it. (2,5)
13 To explode or be fired. (2,3)
15 To make a tree fall by cutting through it is to _____ it down. (4)
16 If you find something bad or illegal and get rid of it, you _____ it out. (4)

ACROSS

3 An aeroplane that is leaving the ground and starting to fly is _____ off. (6)
6 To hit someone or something with a vehicle and drive over them. (3,4)
7 To give money to pay for something, especially when you would prefer not to. (5,2)
9 'This is an expensive place – our money won't _____ .' (2,3)
10 'We have just three days _____ before the beginning of our holiday.' (2,2)
12 If you go _____ someone, you criticize them regularly or for a long time. (2,2)
14 If you _____ up on someone, you get very near them without them expecting it. (5)
15 To continue doing something. (5, 2)
17 Being accepted by a group of people because you are similar to them is called _____ in. (7)
18 To change the time or date of something so that it happens later than originally planned, especially because of a problem. (3,3)

Choosing the right word

1 Style and subject labels

The dictionary gives information about style (e.g. *humorous*, *informal*) and subject areas (e.g. *science*, *business*) in which words may be used in the following way:

> **yeah** /jeə/ adv (*informal*) ★★★ YES

> **merger** /'mɜːdʒə/ noun [C] (*business*) ★ the process of combining two companies or organizations to form a bigger one: *The merger will create the biggest television company in the country.*

Subject labels, such as *business*, *medical* and *journalism*, show that the word is used as part of the language of that subject and that it is not used in normal everyday English. Style labels, such as *informal*, *formal* and *spoken*, show in what situation the word is used. See page 1691 in the dictionary for a complete list of these labels.

▶ **Exercise 78**

Write the correct style label above the groups of words. Check in your dictionary.

> formal   literary   spoken

a _____

   OK   anyway   phew   ouch   hubby

b _____

   thereby   constitute   splendid   notably   duration

c _____

   adieu   joyous   morn   whereupon   dwell

▶ **Exercise 79**

What subject areas do these three groups of nouns belong to? Check your answers in the dictionary.

a	b	c
bid price	perjury	melting point
capital expenditure	limited liability	clone
joint venture	custody	lactic acid
market share	double jeopardy	oxidation
buyout	due process	ecosystem
_____	_____	_____

▶ **Exercise 80**

Each of these six newspaper reports refers to a different sport. Underline the words and phrases that help you to identify the sport. Name the sport. Check in the dictionary.

a _____

> The fourth ball of the seventh over of the final innings of a wonderful Test match may have sounded the death knell to England's aspirations of a fifth successive series win, although their approach last night signalled a belief to the contrary.

b _____

> This was a deserved victory. At the first extra hole the other three were all in trouble, Grunberg having driven into a bunker, Karler hitting his second into the crowd and Hooy, off the best drive of all, finding sand with his second. Levell, though, drew his second round the tree perfectly and ran the ball up to five feet.

c _____

> Running onto Douglas Thorpe's pass in the fourteenth minute, Martin Hayes weaved clear into the penalty area and shot past the goalkeeper. Seven minutes before the interval, Chris Wilkes, the substitute, failed to convert the winger's cross, but it was Taylor's corner 20 minutes from time that Brown headed into his own goal.

d _____

> With 1hr 59 min on the clock, Santos was the width of a racket string away from defeat as Taylor served for the unlikeliest of victories at 5–3. Then during a 26-stroke rally on match point, a Santos forehand clipped the back of the baseline, with many people believing Taylor had won.

e _____

> Johnson, the 6-foot-7-inch senior forward, weighs 215 pounds but moves as fluidly as a guard. At 75–72 he glided down the court, took a pass from Charles Derby and soared to the basket for a shot. Then Douglas dunked for a 77–74.

f _____

> A world record by the women's quartet in the 4 x 200m freestyle crowned an afternoon of top performances at the Short Course Championships in London yesterday. From the start the team were on schedule and by halfway the record was theirs. Other record breakers were Stephen Cock in the 400m medley, Terence Leighton in the 50m backstroke and Liz Wheatley in the 50m butterfly.

▶ **Exercise 81**

Business and finance

Most of the clues and answers in this crossword are connected with business and financial English.

	1		2		3		4		5		6	
⁷M	A	N	U	F	A	C	T	U	R	I	N	G

(Grid positions: 7 across = MANUFACTURING; squares numbered 1–22)

ACROSS

7 The part of a country's economy that comes from the production of goods is called the _____ sector. (13)

8 Business is carried along on the wheels of _____ . (8)

9 The official document that shows who legally owns a building or piece of land is the title _____ . (4)

10 If you _____ your nest, you obtain money for yourself, probably by doing something dishonest. (7)

12 If you are likely to get money or other benefits from an event, you _____ to gain from it. (5)

14 If someone owes you something from an agreement and you demand your _____ of flesh, you take it from them even though this makes them suffer. (5)

16 People who are extremely interested in politics are sometimes called political _____ , especially by people who claim not to be so interested. (7)

19 Before making an important decision, it is useful to undertake a _____-benefit analysis. (4)

20 A shop that sells goods more cheaply than other shops, perhaps too cheaply, is sometimes called a _____ - _____ shop, especially in Britain. (3-5)

22 Consisting of various kinds of people or things. (13)

DOWN

1 Everybody needs to work in order to _____ a living. (4)

2 The month when the Notting Hill Carnival takes place in London. (6)

3 Someone with whom you own a company, and share its profits and losses. (7)

4 To maintain the standard of something is to make sure that it _____ at the same level. (5)

5 When you buy something on _____ , you take it now and pay for it later. (6)

6 The IRS is the American _____ Revenue Service. (8)

11 An increase in the total amount of money gained from the production of goods and services represents _____ growth. (8)

13 Fully automated production uses machines _____ of people. (7)

15 When you decide to leave your job, you have to hand in your _____ to your employer. (6)

17 A company's _____ share is the percentage of the total amount of sales of a particular product that the company has. (6)

18 A very large business is able to sell at lower prices than its smaller competitors because of economies of _____ . (5)

21 A subscription is an amount of money you pay regularly in order to be a member of a _____ . (4)

2 Varieties of English

The dictionary shows the different varieties of English, e.g. British English, Australian English, South African English, Indian English in this way:

> **'chat ,show** noun [C] *Br E* ★ a television or radio programme in which famous people talk about themselves and their work

The dictionary also describes the differences between British and American English. Sometimes different words are used for the same meaning e.g. *pavement/sidewalk, hood/bonnet, crib/cot*. On other occasions the same word has different meanings, e.g. *professor, station, state, couple*. The differences can be very subtle.

> **pavement** /ˈpeɪvmənt/ noun ★★
> **1** [C] *Br E* a path with a hard surface beside a road. *Am E* **sidewalk**
> **2** [U] *Am E* the surface of a road

> **professor** /prəˈfesə/ noun [C] ★★
> **1** *Br E* a senior teacher in a college or university. Someone begins as a **lecturer**, then becomes a **senior lecturer**, then a **reader**, and finally a **professor**: *In 1886 he was appointed professor of physics at the Royal College of Science, London.*
> **2** *Am E* a teacher in a college or university. Someone begins as an **assistant professor**, then becomes an **associate professor**, and finally a **full professor**.

▶ Exercise 82

What varieties of English do you think these words are used in? Check your answers in the dictionary.

a	b	c
Strine	lassi	lass
bushranger	ustad	wee
doona	pandit	loch
walkabout	namaste	bonny
barbie	wallah	laddie

▶ Exercise 83

1 The following words are related to cars and driving. Put each one in the British or American English column.

> petrol station   parking lot   trunk   windscreen
> bonnet   turn signal   emergency brake
> roundabout   gasoline

British English	American English
petrol station	

2 Now write the corresponding words in the other column.

▶ Exercise 84

The following sentences might be different in British and American English.

1 Study them and decide if there is something typically British or American contained in the sentence. Write BE (British English) or AE (American English) next to each sentence. Check in the dictionary.

2 Underline the word you looked up in the dictionary to find the answer.

a A short time <u>afterward</u> the boats arrived at Alexandria bay.   *AE*
b The explosion damaged several buildings and a streetcar. ___
c The lift in the office has been out of order all week. ___
d She lives on delicatessen sandwiches and Chinese takeout. ___
e If I had worked someplace else I may have made more money. ___
f Could you turn the tap off – the water's dripping. ___
g I'm useless at maths. ___
h Simon had the perfect CV for the job. ___
i His relatives showered him with flowers, fruit, candy and toys. ___
j Do you know how to make a paper aeroplane? ___

▶ **Exercise 85**

British and American English

This crossword contains words that are different in British and American English.

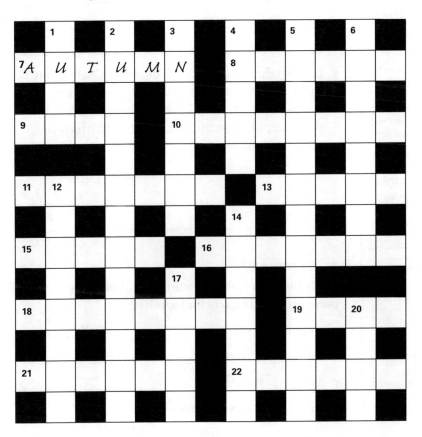

ACROSS

7 The season usually known as *fall* in the US. (6)

8 An American word for a *synagogue*. (6)

9 An American adverb, meaning *extremely*. (4)

10 A *lawyer* in the US. (8)

11 The American equivalent of a British *postcode*. (3, 4)

13 An American *criminal*. (5)

15 The place where British buses are kept when they are not being used. (5)

16 A British English word for a *crepe*. (7)

18 A British English spelling of *ionizing*. (8)

19 When you want to start doing something in the US, you can say 'Let's _____'. (4)

21 An adjective often used in the UK to specify a particular kind of pensioner. (3-3)

22 The American English name for the electrical *earth* wire. (6)

DOWN

1 A British name for a *subway*. (4)

2 This kind of day is usually called *national* in the US and *bank* in the UK. (6,7)

3 *Onward*, as an adverb, in the UK. (7)

4 A British English adjective referring to central government, used in contexts where Americans would use *federal*. (5)

5 *Casualty*, in an American hospital. (9,4)

6 In the US, this might be an answer paper in an exam, a used car price list, or a list of VIPs. It's the colour that's important! (4,4)

12 A British *Popsicle*. (3, 5)

14 In a British railway station this place is called the *left luggage office*. In America it is called the _____ room. (7)

17 British people wait in *queues*. Americans stand in _____ . (5)

20 The American word for *fluff* in the UK means a kind of soft cloth. (4)

3 Synonyms

When two words have roughly the same meaning, they are called synonyms. Few synonyms are completely interchangeable, i.e. they cannot always be used in the same contexts. However, it is useful to think of alternative ways of saying things because this introduces more variety into your language. The dictionary shows words that have similar meanings in the following way:

realistic / ˌrɪəˈlɪstɪk / adj ★★
1 able to understand and accept things as they really are: (PRAGMATIC) *He's never going to agree to that. Be realistic!* ♦ **+about** *The recession has made people more realistic about what they can afford to buy.*

The dictionary also has some boxes at the end of entries that will help you to build your vocabulary and choose the most suitable word for the context.

> **Other ways of saying thin**
>
> **slim** thin in an attractive way: *He was looking much slimmer after his holiday.*
> **slender** thin in a graceful way: *a tall slender woman in her late 40s*
> **skinny** (*informal*) too thin: *a skinny little boy of about eight*
> **anorexic** extremely thin in a way that does not look healthy, also used by doctors to describe someone who has the illness ANOREXIA NERVOSA: *He must have been dieting – he was looking positively anorexic!*
> **lean** thin and strong: *a lean man wearing a cowboy hat*
> **emaciated** extremely thin because you have been ill or do not have enough to eat: *emaciated children holding out bowls for food*
> **trim** thin in a way that suggests you are careful about what you eat and how much you exercise: *His trim figure made him look younger than he was.*
>
> **gaunt** so thin that people can see your bones under your skin: *His face was gaunt with lack of sleep.*
> **bony** so thin that people can see your bones under your skin: *long bony limbs that never seemed to fit his clothes*

▶ **Exercise 86**

1 Think of words with a similar meaning to *trip* (=journey).

_____

_____

_____

2 Look up the noun *trip* in the dictionary. Notice that there are eleven words listed that have a similar meaning to *trip*. What kind of information does the dictionary give you about the context in which you can use them?

_____

_____

_____

▶ **Exercise 87**

Study the other words meaning *trip*. Which is a particular word for *trip* that involves:

a travelling by car? *drive*

b travelling by plane? _____

c going across water? _____

d travelling by bicycle or motorbike? _____

e travelling for research? _____

f an organized trip for a group? _____

g travelling to a place to see specific things of interest? _____

h a long trip in space? _____

▶ **Exercise 88**

At which headword do you think you would find the box that has *ad, commercial, billboard* and *flyer*? Check in the dictionary.

_____

► **Exercise 89**

Look up the word *agree*. What is another way of saying you agree with someone:

a strongly

_____

b with some reservation

_____

c when in fact you may disagree

_____

► **Exercise 90**

Write down all the words you can think of that mean *bad*. Fill in the blanks in the sentences, trying to use a different word each time. If you need help, check the box in the dictionary for *bad*.

a My son suffered a very _serious_ injury playing football.

b She is fairly _____ learner of languages.

c Her uncle is a rather _____ man.

d He is a very _____ guitarist.

e The film we saw last night was really _____ .

f Her little boy's behaviour is truly _____ .

g I've got a really _____ headache.

► **Exercise 91**

1 Think of all the words you know that mean *famous*. Try to remember what contexts each of them is used in. Then check the box for *famous* in the dictionary.

_____

_____

_____

2 Now read these sentences and decide which would be the best word to complete them with.

a Charlie Chaplin was a _____ film star.

b Al Capone was a _____ American gangster.

c David Beckham is a _____ footballer.

d Her husband is an _____ professor of chemistry.

4 Antonyms

The dictionary also shows words that mean approximately the opposite (i.e. antonyms) in the following way:

> **descent** /dɪˈsent/ noun ★
> **1** [C/U] the act of moving down to a lower place or position: *The plane made a sudden descent.* **1a.** [C] a road or path that slopes down —opposite ASCENT

► **Exercise 92**

1 Read the sentences and notice the meaning of the underlined words.

a It sounds like she's very <u>interested</u> in daily politics.   *uninterested*

b Forecasts show that the euro will prove <u>firm</u> against other major currencies.   _____

c Fate had put here <u>in the wrong place at the wrong time</u> with the wrong man.   _____

d Peter is <u>sociable</u> and popular.   _____

e I followed the road, enjoying the <u>firm</u> surface after crossing the marsh.   _____

f The new tax system was generally <u>disliked</u> by the public.   _____

g The drive took them over <u>rough</u> terrain.   _____

h He's a <u>proud</u> and intolerant man.   _____

i The <u>interior</u> of the cathedral has been finely preserved.   _____

j The evidence doesn't support what they claim to be <u>true</u>.   _____

2 Now write a word or phrase with the opposite meaning to those underlined. Check in the dictionary.

▶ **Exercise 93**

Synonyms

The answers in this crossword are synonyms of the words in the clues.

ACROSS

8 present (4)

9 brave (10)

10 spit (6)

11 magician (8)

12 cab (4)

13 constraint (10)

17 wedding band (4)

18 dewy-eyed (5)

19 gainsay (4)

20 jobless (10)

22 pontiff (4)

23 barrier (8)

27 florid (6)

28 false (10)

29 possesses (4)

DOWN

1 detaching (10)

2 determining (8)

3 casual (10)

4 pluck (4)

5 just (4)

6 loathe (6)

7 impolite (4)

14 hirsute (5)

15 buns (5,5)

16 all-powerful (10)

19 rely on (6,2)

21 network (6)

24 belch (4)

25 French fry (4)

26 way out (4)

Language study

1 Background information

The dictionary gives additional background information about words in boxes. For example, for the words *Monopoly money* and *bowler hat*, the following information is given:

> From Monopoly, a game in which players use large amounts of toy money to buy streets, houses, and hotels.

> Bowler hats are thought of as being typical of CIVIL SERVANTS and businessmen in the UK, but in fact they are rarely worn any more and are considered old-fashioned.

▶ **Exercise 94**

Use the background box in the dictionary to answer these questions.

a Pandora's box
What might happen when you open Pandora's box?

_____

b Boxing Day
When is Boxing Day and why is it called that?

_____

_____

c catch-22
What kind of problem does this refer to?

_____

d Big Brother
Who is Big Brother?

_____

e Downing Street
Who lives in this street?

_____

▶ **Exercise 95**

1 New words are constantly being created by combining existing words. Look at the words below and guess what two words they are made up from.

a <u>*Bombay*</u>	Bollywood	<u>*Hollywood*</u>
b _____	netizen	_____
c _____	screenager	_____
d _____	docudrama	_____
e _____	netiquette	_____
f _____	docusoap	_____

2 Match the definitions (1–6) with the words above (a–f). Check in the dictionary.

1 someone who spends a lot of time using the World Wide Web _____

2 a television programme or film based on events that really happened _____

3 the polite way of expressing yourself or communicating with other people when you are using the World Wide Web _____

4 the Indian film industry _____

5 a television programme series about the lives of real people _____

6 a young person who spends a lot of time using computers and the World Wide Web _____

2 Metaphors

You may have learnt about metaphor as a literary feature, but metaphor is also woven into our use of language. It is typical of both written and spoken English. Here is an example of images of *money* used to speak of time:

> **Metaphor**
> Money is like **food**, which gets eaten or is shared out. The same idea is used to talk about other types of resource.
>
> *They didn't get a fair* **share/slice of the cake/pie**. ♦ *The rent* **takes a large bite out of** *their income.* ♦ *The fees have* **swallowed** *most of my grant.* ♦ *This* **ate into** *our savings.* ♦ *The richest nations* **gobble up/devour** *the world's resources.* ♦ *The company was* **starved** *of investment capital.* ♦ *The government said that* **the cupboard was bare.** ♦ *We have to make do with* **scraps from** *their* **table**.

Notice:

1 that these metaphors are in bold type;

2 that these metaphors can be one word or more than one word;

3 that these metaphors are mostly verbs, nouns and adjectives.

▶ **Exercise 96**

1 Study the metaphor box for each of these words:

   a quality   **b** conversation   **c** search

2 Notice that:

   a the words and phrases express large quantities as if they were large amounts of water;

   b the words and phrases show that conversation is like a journey;

   c the words and phrases connect searching with hunting and digging.

▶ **Exercise 97**

1 Choose one of the words in the box below to complete the sentences (a–e) in the table.

2 Find two example sentences (1–10) that illustrate this metaphor in use.

important   angry   understanding   power   happy

	Example sentences
a Being _angry_ is like being hot or on fire.	2, 6
b Feeling _____ and hopeful is like being high up or like moving upwards.	
c Being _____ is like being large or heavy.	
d Having _____ and controlling someone is like being in a higher position than them.	
e _____ something is like seeing it.	

1 She holds the **highest** position in the company.
2 They were having a **blazing/flaming** row.
3 How many people are there **above** you?
4 There was a change in the public **perception** of education.
5 I've been **walking/floating on air** ever since.
6 It made my blood **boil**.
7 He is the **greatest** writer of the twentieth century.
8 I was **over the moon** when they told me.
9 I **see what you mean**.
10 Her ideas **carry** a lot of **weight** with the boss.

If you would like to learn more about metaphor in English, turn to pages LA8 and LA9 in your dictionary.

Exploring a dictionary page

▶ **Exercise 98**

Look up page 310 in the dictionary. Study the page and see how quickly you can find the answers to these questions.

a What are wine corks made of?

_____

_____

b Where does cork come from?

_____

_____

c What is the meaning of the verb *corkscrew*?

_____

_____

d Does corked wine taste pleasant?

_____

_____

e Which syllable has the main stress in the compound *corned beef*?

_____

_____

f What is the difference between the British and American meaning of the drink *cordial*?

_____

_____

g What is the difference between the British and American word *corn*?

_____

_____

_____

h How many red words are there on this page? What are they?

_____

_____

i Which of these red words occurs most frequently in English?

_____

_____

j How many names of animals are there on this page?

_____

_____

k What is a short word for trousers made of corduroy?

_____

_____

l What particle is used with the verb *cordon*?

_____

_____

m How many meanings are given for the noun *corner*?

_____

_____

n What prepositions are used with the first meaning of *corner*?

_____

_____

o In which form of art is the word *Corinthian* often used?

_____

_____

p What are some collocations that use the noun *corner*?

_____

_____

Working with texts

▶ **Exercise 99**

Read the article and answer the questions.

Funny Old World

1   'I don't know why they kept me so long in prison',
2   seventy-six-year old Ivan Boroughs told reporters
3   from his home. 'I'm just glad to be out. I did not enjoy
4   staying there. I am looking forward to living a good
5   life now, but it was a long time to be in gaol, and I am
6   still upset.'
7   Boroughs, who had been charged with malicious
8   destruction of property in December 1972, had
9   spent nearly twenty-nine years in prison without trial
10 for allegedly smashing a pane of glass in a bank. A
11 prison official explained that 'at first, Mr Boroughs
12 was deemed mentally ill, and therefore unfit to stand
13 trial. He was remanded in custody, and soon got
14 better, and we all waited to be told what to do next.
15 But nobody ever told us'.
16   The Commissioner of Corrections, John Prescod,
17 confirmed that officials had known that Boroughs
18 was in prison. 'We were monitoring his progress
19 yearly, but we had to wait on communication from
20 the court, and that did not come until Tuesday. It's
21 ironic, really, because if he had been charged and
22 found guilty, the maximum sentence would have
23 been three years.'

a What is a more common spelling for *gaol*? (line 5)

_____

b Does *prisoner* mean the same as *jailer*?

_____

c Look up the word *prison*. What is the phrase describing a person in prison for their political beliefs or actions?

_____

d Look at the entry for *prison*. What word is used to describe the time someone spends in prison?

_____

e Underline the word you would look up in the dictionary to find the meaning of the following phrases. Then check in your dictionary.

  1 remand in custody (line 13)   _____

  2 stand trial (line 12)   _____

  3 find someone guilty (line 22)   _____

f Which of these materials can the three words below be used with?

glass	metal	paper	plastic	wood

  1 a sheet of   *glass*_____   _____

                    _____   _____

  2 a splinter of   _____   _____

  3 a pane of   _____

g The dictionary gives five meanings for the word *correction*. Which is the meaning used in line 16?

_____

h Look at the title of the article. Find *funny old world* in the dictionary. What does this idiom mean?

_____

_____

_____

i What are two possible synonyms for *funny* used in this sense?

_____   _____

j Notice that there are 24 meanings of *out* in the dictionary. Which sense corresponds to the meaning of *be out* used in the passage? (line 3)

_____

_____

k Could *ironic* be replaced by *ironical* in the text? (line 21)

_____

l How many meanings of the word *sentence* do you know? Do you expect *sentence* to be a red word? Check in the dictionary. (line 22)

_____

_____

_____

▶ **Exercise 100**

Read the story and answer the questions.

The Memory Man

1   The brother of the secretary of our local philately
2   society went on holiday to America in the 1980s and
3   hit the heritage trail as soon as he arrived: Wild West
4   ghost towns, War of Independence landmarks,
5   Japanese car manufacturers ... the lot.
6   One day the tour guide directed his charges
7   to a native American reservation, where he
8   recommended that the limey visitors check out the
9   legendary local 'memory man', a grey, gnarled old
10 American Indian who made Keith Richards look
11 like Tom Cruise. He could remember the most
12 incredible everyday detail from the last sixty years,
13 the guide assured them.
14   Having crossed the old fellow's palm with the
15 requisite silver, the tourist then posed the single
16 question he was permitted to ask: 'What did you
17 have for breakfast twenty-five years ago today?'
18 he queried. 'Two eggs', said the old chief,
19 enigmatically. With no way to disprove this, the Brit
20 withdrew, not particularly impressed.
21   Eight years later, on another jaunt across
22 the Americas, the same tourist found himself driving
23 through familiar territory – he was near the
24 reservation with the amazing antique recollector.
25 'Ah ha,' he thought, 'Let's see how good his
26 memory really is – I wonder if he'll remember me.'
27   Making his way to the old moth-eaten teepee, the
28 visitor slipped inside and sat down unannounced
29 opposite the ancient sage. Then he greeted him as he
30 saw fit, beginning, 'How!'
31   'Scrambled,' muttered the old man, sucking
32 serenely on his pipe.

a List some nouns and adjectives that refer to the
memory man in the text.

nouns	adjectives
fellow	_____
_____	_____
_____	_____
_____	_____

b The author constructs the word *recollector*. What two
words is this derived from? (line 24)

_____   _____

c Five of the words in the line below form an idiomatic
expression. Which five? What does the idiom mean?

*Having crossed the old fellow's palm with the requisite
silver ...* (lines 14, 15)

_____

_____

d What do members of a *philately* society do? (line 1)

_____

e At which headwords do you think you would find these
words in the dictionary?

                      headword

1 enigmatically (line 19)   _____
2 moth-eaten (line 27)   _____
3 scrambled (line 31)   _____
4 serenely (line 32)   _____

f Where in the dictionary can you find an illustration for
the meaning of *scrambled* used in the passage? (line 31)

_____

g Find two words in the text that refer to someone who
comes from Great Britain.

_____   _____

h What are the differences between the two words?

_____

i How many words in the dictionary begin with the
spelling *gn*? List these words. What is the first sound in
each word?

_____

_____

j What is another spelling of *teepee*? (line 27)

_____

k The dictionary gives six meanings of *lot*. Which is used
in the story? (line 5)

_____

l What does *the lot* refer to in the text? (line 5)

_____

m Look at the menu for the word *charge¹* in the dictionary.
How many meanings of *charge* do you know? Which
meaning corresponds to the use of charge in the story?
(line 6)

_____

▶ **Exercise 101**

Read the article and answer the questions.

Into the Abyss

1 IT'S DEADLY DARK, wet, and you're chilled right
2 through. You haven't drawn a breath for a couple of
3 minutes now, and your heart is barely beating. Your
4 lungs have been crushed until they take up little more
5 space than a Coke can, and although your spleen has
6 splurged out a mass of extra blood cells, your veins
7 have collapsed and the blood has been forced out of
8 your limbs into the space where your lungs should be.
9 What little oxygen you have left is devoted only to
10 keeping your heart and brain ticking over, and there's an
11 intolerable pain as your eardrums feel about to burst.

12 Competitive freediving pushes the body to the
13 absolute limits of endurance. From the very first
14 moment cold water hits the face, your body starts
15 behaving differently. Blood vessels in the muscles, skin
16 and internal organs contract, channelling pretty much
17 all the available oxygen to our two most vital organs –
18 the heart and brain. At the same time, the heart slows
19 down. To survive a deep dive you need this efficient
20 diving response, and as big a lungful of air as you can
21 manage. Some divers have even learnt to swallow air
22 into their already full lungs. It's not just to keep up the
23 oxygen supply, but also to cope with the increasing
24 pressure. For every 10 metres you descend, the
25 pressure rises by 1 atmosphere, and the air in the lungs
26 is compressed to match.

27 The quest for greater depths is sure to continue –
28 Francisco 'Pipin' Ferreras has already claimed an
29 unofficial record of 162 metres. But each body and
30 each day is different. Breath-hold diving is a wonderful
31 thing. But no researcher would say it's safe to go so far
32 or so deep. It's a very, very fine line they are treading at
33 those depths.

a Note the use of the word *abyss* in the title. Find the corresponding meaning in the dictionary.

_____

b There are six nouns related to the body in the first paragraph. Identify them and check their meaning in the dictionary.

noun	verb		noun	verb
1 *heart*	_____	4	_____	_____
2 _____	_____	5	_____	_____
3 _____	_____	6	_____	_____

c Notice the verbs that are used with each noun in the passage. Write them in the table above.

d Now look up these verbs in the dictionary. What image or meaning do they add to the nouns?

_____

e Look up the word *very*. Which sense of the word is used in the passage? (line 13)

_____

f Which of the following body parts can combine with *-ful* and *of*? Check your dictionary and give an example for each.

lung	eye	ear	head	arm	hand
fist	mouth	nose			

lungful _____   *lungful of air* _____

_____   _____

_____   _____

_____   _____

g What kind of search does the word *quest* refer to? (line 27)

_____

h Check the underlined expression to see what it means in the context. (line 32)
It's a very, very <u>fine line they are treading</u> at those depths.

_____

i Find the opposite of *descend* in the dictionary. (line 24)

_____

j Which syllable is stressed in the word *record* in the text? (line 29)

_____

k What phrase is the adjective *breath-hold* derived from? (line 30)

_____

l Where can you find this expression in the dictionary?

_____

m There are two words in the text that refer to the deepest parts of the sea. Find them and say what the similarities and differences are between their uses.

_____   _____

_____

_____

_____

n Find another way of saying *devote to* in the dictionary. (line 9)

_____

o Name the two different types of *blood vessels* in the body. Check in the dictionary.

_____   _____

Class activities

The dictionary offers a good source of material for class work in the form of exploration, discussion and the development of independent learning skills.

All the exercises in this workbook can be used either as individual or as class activities. When used as class activities, it may be helpful to write the exercise on the board, to ask students to consult their dictionaries, and then to write up their suggested answers on the board for discussion.

Here are some specific class activities for developing dictionary skills with some tips on dictionary work in the classroom.

▶ **Exercise 102**

The dictionary game – meanings

> **Aim**
> Developing skill in using definitions and examples; sensitizing students to hints about the meanings of words; team game

Steps

- Divide the class into teams of 2–5 students. Give each team a word that is in the dictionary and which they probably do not know. Each team should have a different word. For example, *corpulent*, or *corncrake*, or *corer*.
- Ask each team to check the definition of the word in the dictionary, and to find an example sentence containing that word.
- Then ask each team to make up two false definitions for the word. Suppose the team has the word *corer*, then they might have the following, of which 2 is correct (taken from the dictionary), and 1 and 3 are false (made up by the team).

  1 The room in a church where the choir gets ready.

  2 A small tool used for taking out the centre of fruit such as apples.

  3 The name given to a crow that makes a lot of noise early in the morning.

- When they are ready, each team reads its word, and the three definitions, as if they all could be true. The other teams try to deduce or guess the correct definition without using the dictionary.

> **Hints & tips**
>
> When your students use the dictionary, use it yourself. This helps you to give them the time they need and enables you to understand problems they may find.

▶ **Exercise 103**

The dictionary game – word stress patterns

> **Aim**
> Developing skill in using and practising the pronunciation information in the dictionary; team game

Steps

- This game is similar to the one in Exercise 102, but this time the teams find three stress patterns for their word, one which is correct, and two which are false.
- Give each team a word of three or more syllables. For example, *hypothesis*.
- Ask each team to prepare and rehearse three different stress patterns for the word, for example:

  1 /haɪˈpɒθəsɪs/

  2 /ˈhaɪpɒθəsɪs/

  3 /haɪpɒθəˈsɪs/

- When they are ready, they write the word on the board, in normal spelling, and then say each of the three pronunciations aloud. The other teams try to guess which pronunciation or stress pattern is most probable, and check with their dictionaries. This requires awareness of the use of phonemic symbols and the sounds they represent. It is also good practice in the conscious placement of stress.

> **Hints & tips**
>
> Keep an eye open for ways of integrating the dictionary in your class work. Wherever possible, have students get information from the dictionary themselves, rather than you telling them.

▶ **Exercise 104**

The distribution of first letters in the dictionary

Aim

Sensitizing students to the distribution and location of first letters in an English dictionary, and hence to finding entries more quickly; handling and turning pages

Steps

• Hold the dictionary clearly in front of you, as if you are about to open and use it, so that students can see only the top edge of the pages. Make sure all the class can see the dictionary. Open it at any page, and ask the class to guess which letter is open in front of you. Repeat this a few times and then ask them to try it with each other. Ask the class questions such as *Which letter is in the middle of the dictionary? Which letter do you think has the most/fewest pages?*

• Ask them which are the most frequent first letters in their mother tongue if they use Latin script.

▶ **Exercise 105**

Alphabetization

Aim

Developing the basic skill of dictionary searching

Steps

• Take any ten consecutive words from any page in the dictionary. Put them on the board in random (i.e. non-alphabetical) order. For example:

swami   swansong   sward   swallow   swam

swank   swamp   swan   swap   swanky

• Allow students a few seconds only to look at them, and then ask them to call the words out aloud in alphabetical order.

  Hints & tips

Help the class to understand the dictionary entry by discussing it as a class activity. Sometimes it is useful to write part of an entry on the board in order to notice the key features of the entry and to work on it together.

▶ **Exercise 106**

Guessing a word from the definition

Aim

Using menu definitions to understand the language of definitions, and to gain insight into multiple meanings of single words

Steps

• Take a menu from the dictionary and write the short definitions on the board, like this:

1 *go in particular direction*

2 *be in control of group*

3 *be first in a list/line*

4 *put title at top*

5 *hit ball with head*

• Divide the class into groups and ask them to examine the short definitions to guess which word the menu is describing. They write their suggestions on the board, discuss them, and then check in the dictionary. (The word in this example is *head*.)

• Here is another example:

1 *difficult to live in*

2 *about actions/words*

3 *about sounds/lights etc*

4 *facts: unpleasant & true*

5 *substances: damaging*

(The word in this example is *harsh*.)

  Hints & tips

Start a lesson by giving students several items to investigate in the dictionary, items which will come up in your lesson anyway. This will encourage participation and interest. You can start this activity while waiting for any late arrivals.

▶ **Exercise 107**
Using examples to notice similar and different meanings

> **Aim**
> Discriminating different meanings of the same word form

Steps

- Take a word with multiple meanings. Look at the dictionary example for each meaning and write another example yourself for each word so that now you have two examples for each meaning. For instance, for the different meanings of the word *corner*, you can give the following examples:

dictionary examples

  1 Watch the baby – that table has sharp corners.

  2 I get my newspaper from the shop on the corner.

  3 Let's find a quiet corner and talk about it.

other examples written by you

  a Mind your head on the corner.

  b There's an excellent pub on the corner.

  c Here's a nice corner to sit in.

- Give each student one of the example sentences and invite them to move around and find who has the example which contains the same meaning as their own, so that they match **1** with **a**. When they have done this, ask them to check with the dictionary.

> **Hints & tips**
>
> Invite students to use the dictionary to check words they already know. This encourages them to extend their knowledge and provides insights into how the dictionary works.

▶ **Exercise 108**
Guessing the word from the example

> **Aim**
> Developing skill in using dictionary examples; using hints from the context about the meanings of words

Steps

- Take a frequent (red) word you want your class to study, and find the examples that are given for each meaning of that word in the dictionary.

- Write out the examples but remove the word, leaving a blank. Where there is more than one meaning, provide examples for each meaning, with the word itself blanked out. Here are some examples with different forms of the same word blanked out in each.

  1 Three people died in the fire, but John _____ through the bedroom window.

  2 Two security guards _____ injury in the attack.

  3 His name _____ me right now.

  4 About five tonnes of crude oil had _____ into the sea.

  5 We're hoping to _____ to the Algarve in May.

- Read or show the examples with blanks to the class. Invite students to discuss them and guess the blank word, explaining their choice. Though this example has the same word removed from each sentence, each has a different meaning in the example. (The word is *escape*.)

> **Hints & tips**
>
> Don't expect students to remember everything they look up. They can easily look it up again.

▶ **Exercise 109**
Background information

> **Aim**
> Using the boxes that give background information

Steps

- Find several boxes giving background information about words in the dictionary. For example:

  Good Samaritan   Cinderella   Home Alone

- Write out the text in the box removing the keyword and ask the class to identify the missing names (and objects). For example:

  1 From the Bible story of the _____ who helped an injured man that no one else would help.

2 _____ is the main character in a famous children's story. She is a poor girl, badly treated by her stepsisters, but in the end, thanks to the power of magic, she is able to marry the rich attractive Prince Charming.

3 From the US film _____ , in which a boy is accidentally left alone at home without his parents.

Hints & tips

The more often your students use the dictionary, the more use they will find for it. Have fun with the dictionary, and enjoy the discoveries and surprises!

▶ **Exercise 110**
Putting phrases into dialogues and dramas

Aim
Looking up idioms, phrases and collocations; understanding their meaning, and writing them into a short dialogue or drama

Steps

• Give each group a (different) typical phrase, for example:

eat out   eat up   eat your words

when do you want to eat   what would you like to eat

• Invite students to make a small dialogue or drama which uses and illustrates the meaning of that phrase, as given in the dictionary. Then each group performs its mini-drama or dialogue, while the others watch, and try to guess the meaning of the phrase.

Hints & tips

Don't hurry students when using the dictionary. Encourage them to take an interest in exploring the dictionary, and in noticing other things.

▶ **Exercise 111**
Phrasal verbs

Aim
Drawing attention to the use and meaning of phrasal verbs; finding them in the dictionary

Steps

• Select some common verbs that make many phrasal verbs. For example:

stand   add   take   see

• Give each team one verb and several particles. For example:

back   in   off   out   over   to   up

• Ask them to make as many two-word phrasal verbs (i.e. verb + particle) as they think are possible, and to guess the meanings based on their own experience of English, then to check in the dictionary to see if that phrasal verb exists, and if so what it means. They can also find or make an example of that phrasal verb in use.

▶ **Exercise 112**
Phrasal verbs with adverbs and prepositions

Aim
Drawing attention to the use and meaning of verbs with adverbs and prepositions; finding them in the dictionary

Steps

• This is a similar activity to the one in Exercise 111, but this time select some common verbs that are used with adverbs and prepositions together (e.g look up to, give up on).

• Give each team one verb and several adverbs and prepositions. For example:

give   take   look

away   down   for   forward   from   in   on

out   over   to   up

• Ask students to make as many three-word phrasal verbs as they can, and to guess the meanings based on their own experience of English, then to check in the dictionary to see if that phrasal verb exists, and if so what it means. They can also find or make an example of that phrasal verb in use.

▶ **Exercise 113**

Working with concordances – definitions

Aim

Reminding students that words often have several meanings; getting students used to looking carefully at language

Steps

- Ask students to form groups and give them the word in the concordance (*note*). Explain that they need to list all the meanings they know for that word and to write a definition for each of the meanings.

- When they are ready, distribute the copies of the concordance (below) to the groups. Ask students to

look at the example sentences in the concordance and decide if there are any more meanings shown. Ask them to list these meanings and revise their definitions if necessary, using the examples.

- When the groups are ready, ask them to compare their answers with the definitions given in the dictionary.

Hints & tips

Where possible, allow students to use their dictionaries in tests and exams. Make dictionary usage part of any test you write. The ability to use a learners' dictionary must be a relevant component of language ability.

#	Concordance
1	e highest denomination will be 200-zloty notes , to be introduced later this year. One U.
2	ospital that my father had requested the notes . A psychiatrist, he had a theory that my
3	u letters from the children themselves, a note from the teacher outlining the benefits o
4	reveled outside in spring weather to the notes of traditional Portuguese music provide
5	and he wanted to learn). He took lots of notes and after three days he said, 'Raymond
6	o Israel. The show ends on an uncertain note . Many of the contemporary artists are n
7	t of him which contained £250,000 in old notes . 'They were old and shredded but it cr
8	e managed to do it? Did you leave him a note ? Or did you just ask him to do it? I wrote
9	n Gregory of Tours, but with more than a note of hostility. Chilperic is compared with N
10	a four-inch blade and demanded all the notes from the till. Mr Freeman explained tha
11	ssues not only about the way therapists' notes could be misused in court but about the
12	the five finger exercise, let's see what a note on the piano sounds like instead of playi
13	nch and handed the female employee a note , which read 'This is an armed robbery,
14	e year old Darren, say they withdraw the notes from a bank and didn't know they were
15	time. I'd just like to end on an optimistic note . I think this has been a terrifically inform
16	rts on the wall and we went through our notes and we tried to identify points of conses
17	his home at about 4.30pm. There was a note telling me both Jack and Pat, his wife, w
18	David Wylie. The second half ended on a note of controversy when John Barrett was o
19	out his harmonica and play all the wrong notes ? Now he's Bruce Willis,' Levi says. Fa
20	photographed the participants and took notes on what was said. China also has been
21	stomer buying a 40p postcard with a £50 note , I wonder what I can usefully tell any bo
22	all been good ideas. I sound one warning note about individual choice – it works in tow
23	notoriously difficult for singers as the top note reached 'F in alt'. One comic in the clas
24	to date. No longer is it any use making a note in your diary at home about the meal yo
25	pe you'll pardon me if I play a few wrong notes .'' Mistakes or not, the audience gave h

▶ **Exercise 114**

Working with concordances – definitions, collocations and grammar

Aim

Looking at the environment of a word; getting students used to looking carefully at language

Steps

- Distribute the copies of the concordance (below) to different groups of students. Ask them to draw conclusions about the meaning of the keyword, to write their own definitions, and to make any observations about the grammatical behaviour of the word and any other words it occurs with.

- Ask the groups to compare notes, and then to check their conclusions with the dictionary.

Hints & tips

Set students the homework task of adding to their vocabulary five or so words of their own choice. They can choose the words and then investigate them in terms of spelling, pronunciation, stress, usage, meaning, context etc.

#	Concordance
1	ary possible risk because their clients put faith in them but they also climb as do some
2	able them to fully integrate their religious faith in their lives. The approach of the histori
3	, Cr Whan said part of his plan to restore faith in council hinged on his agreement with
4	haracter in the Novel' she expresses her faith in the power of the computer as a conce
5	sentially unhealthy lifestyle; she had little faith in medical expertise and liked to recall t
6	nd I intend to do it. The club have shown faith in me and that kind of backing deserves
7	important factors in the painful losses of faith which Victorians underwent. Despite the
8	est baptized the babies into the Christian faith . He brought the children to the bishop f
9	fered DNA samples, it could help restore faith in the safety of the community by knowi
10	e Christians who had been of the Jewish faith , and those who were converted Gentile
11	ng their decisions. How can people have faith in us if we hold our job to redress the gri
12	ed. As his theory suggests, Larry has lost faith in traditional psychiatry. If the discourse
13	othing of the serious fraud. They put their faith and money in a bank that was being mo
14	en said, only through their deep religious faith – and that that has been a great lesson
15	nk God there is someone ... restored my faith in human nature ... performed a signal s
16	riatrics from the first team and placed his faith , and his future, in the hands of youngst
17	about a presidential candidate's personal faith and what role, if any, it has in the very p
18	proponents cross examined. I have great faith in locally-elected planning committees,
19	eks have seen many big investors losing faith in the euro and shifting their money back
20	week, looking for ways to strengthen the faith of believers and spreading the church's
21	redictability that it must have restored the faith of the most hardened football cynic end
22	nterest in the election and they've got no faith in any of parties they all seemed to muc
23	This is to misrepresent religion. Religious faith is based on what is believed to be true.
24	, John. Thanks for the mail – I hadn't lost faith in you at all – was just hoping that you ha
25	spect, because, while she respected the faith of religious people and found religious id

▶ **Exercise 115**

Exploring a dictionary page – scanning

> **Aim**
> Scanning a dictionary page for specific information;
> developing skill in focusing on specific elements of a
> dictionary entry

Steps

• Ask students to study page 498 in the dictionary and
hand out a copy of the questions (below). When they
are ready, they compare their answers in pairs and
then check with the dictionary.

- ✂ - -

a Where is the primary stress in the compounds
beginning *fairy...*?

_____

b Where is the primary stress in the compounds
beginning *faith...*?

_____

c What is the convention concerning the use of *Yours
faithfully* at the end of a formal letter?

_____

_____

_____

d How many red words are there on this page?

_____

e How many of these red words have three stars?

_____

f What word class can the word *fake* be?

_____

g Which other words would you look up to find out more
about:

1 *falafel*   **2** *fajita*

_____   _____

h What do people use a *falcon* for?

_____

i How does the addition of *-er* or *-ry* change the word
falcon?

_____

j How many meanings are listed for the verb *fall*?

_____

k Which meaning is shown in the picture?

_____

l What are the opposites given for meanings 2, 8 and 9?

_____

m Which meaning of *fall* is to do with dates? What
preposition is used?

_____

_____

n What prepositions may be used with the verb *fall* to
mean 'lose a position of power'?

_____

- ✂ - -

▶ **Exercise 116**

Exploring a dictionary page – writing questions

> **Aim**
> Scanning a dictionary page; developing skill in
> interpreting specific elements of a dictionary entry

Steps

• Ask students to turn to a particular page in the
dictionary or hand out a copy of a dictionary page to
each student. Invite them to study the page and write
ten questions relating to the entries on the page
(similar to those in Exercise 115).

• When they are ready, ask them to exchange questions
with a partner and to answer them.

• Alternatively, invite a student to ask the question to the
whole class.

Answer key

Finding words in the dictionary

1 Alphabetical ordering

▶ **Exercise 1**

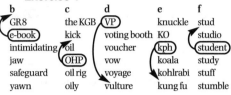

b	c	d	e	f
GR8	the KGB	VP	knuckle	stud
e-book	kick	voting booth	KO	studio
intimidating	oil	voucher	kph	student
jaw	OHP	vow	koala	study
safeguard	oil rig	voyage	kohlrabi	stuff
yawn	oily	vulture	kung fu	stumble

▶ **Exercise 2**

a	b	c
world-famous	persist	evacuate
WP	perspective	honeymoon
wrapping paper	PG	ID card
wreckage	phone number	press-up
write-off	piggy bank	queen bee
wrong	playground	round-trip

▶ **Exercise 3**

b	T-junction	c	TLC	d	TM
e	TMT	f	TNT	g	to
h	toad	i	toad-in-the-hole	j	toadstool
k	toady	l	to and fro	m	toast
n	toaster	o	toastie	p	toasting fork

2 Guide words

▶ **Exercise 4**

Yes b, c, d, f, g   No a, e, h, i, j, k

▶ **Exercise 5**

a stout, storey, story, stove
b straight, straighten, straight away, straight-faced
c strain, stranger, strand, strap

▶ **Exercise 6**

Example answers
a legal, legacy, legally, legend, legislation
b loveless, lovely, lover, loving, low
c journalism, journalist, journey, joy, jubilee
d usual, usually, utility, utter, utterly

▶ **Exercise 7**

3 Checking spellings

▶ **Exercise 8**

b phantom	c unconscious	d lacquer
e believe	f bankruptcy	g piece
h restaurant	i stomach	j moustache
k conscience	l proceed	

4 Alternative spellings

▶ **Exercise 9**

	1 Write the alternative spelling.	2 Is the alternative American English?	3 Is the alternative British English?
c icon		☑	☐
d tyre		☐	☐
e racket		☐	☑
f swap		☑	☐
g jewellery		☐	☐
h hippie		☐	☑
i baptize		☐	☐
j inquiry		☐	☑
k unrecognizable		☐	☐
l OK		☑	☐
m programme		☐	☐
n nosy		☐	☐
o tsar		☐	☑
p moisturize		☑	☐
q colour		☑	☐
r catalogue		☐	☑
s encyclopedia		☐	☐

5 Abbreviations

▶ **Exercise 10**

b yr	c co	d Ltd	e n/a	f St
g ono	h min.	i d.o.b	j c/o

Red words and black words

▶ **Exercise 11**

One, two or three.

▶ **Exercise 12**

There are eight red words on these pages:
paper[1], paperback, paperwork, par[1], parade[1], paradise, paragraph[1], parallel[1].

▶ **Exercise 13**

lapse, etiquette, pen, missive

▶ **Exercise 14**

The entries for red words are longer than the entries for black words. The entries for red words contain more meanings and more information about the usage of these words.

Introducing concordances

▶ **Exercise 15**

jam (noun)
1 sweet sticky food: 3, 8, 13
2 difficult situation: 9, 15, 20
3 line of stopped vehicles: 1, 7, 14, 16, 19, 23
jam (verb)
1 put in small place: 4, 10, 17, 25
2 difficult to move: 2, 5, 11, 18, 24
3 block movement: 6, 21, 22
7 make music in group: 12

▶ **Exercise 16**

a The word has four meanings:
1 body part: 2, 6, 11, 16, 18, 25
2 unit of length: 3, 4, 7, 12, 15, 19, 20
3 bottom of something: 5, 8, 10, 14, 22, 23
4 end of something: 1, 9, 13, 17, 21, 24

b
1 body part

c
4 end of something

Pronunciation and stress

1 Pronunciation guide

▶ **Exercise 17**

a 22   b 25

▶ **Exercise 18**

Example answers

same as a letter in the English alphabet	different from any letter in the English alphabet
p	ʒ
b	ŋ
i	əʊ
d	ð
e	ɔː

▶ **Exercise 19**

Example answers

a /eɪ/ bay, aim	b /j/ you, cute
c /ʌ/ cut, uncle	d /θ/ thin, growth
e /əʊ/ go, poet	f /ʃ/ shine, harsh
g /ɔː/ caught, law	

2 Using the phonetic key

▶ **Exercise 21**

1 foot, bush, goods
2 fool, cool, do
3 oar, thorn, floor

▶ **Exercise 22**

b /θruː/ c /eɪk/ d /mɔːl/, /mæl/ e /heə/
f /kɪk/ g /sɒŋ/ h /waɪl/   i /beɪð/
j /tɒs/

▶ **Exercise 23**

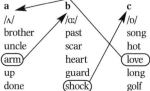

a /ʌ/	b /ɑː/	c /ɒ/
brother	past	song
uncle	scar	hot
arm	heart	love
up	guard	long
done	shock	golf

▶ **Exercise 24**
/ʌ/   enough, tough, rough
/ɔː/   brought, bought, thought, fought
/aʊ/   bough, plough, drought
/əʊ/   dough, though
/uː/   through

▶ **Exercise 25**
b representative   c practically
d sophisticated   e Although
f poisonous

3 Silent letters
▶ **Exercise 26**
b com(b)   c pa(l)m   d (g)nome   e (k)nee
f sa(l)mon   g p(s)yche   h (p)neumonia
i autum(n)   j i(s)land   k (k)nob   l fas(t)en

4 Saying abbreviations
▶ **Exercise 27**

	1 say each letter separately	2 say it as an acronym	3 say the full form of the word	write the full form of the word
b	☐	☐	☑	attention
c	☑	☐	☐	before Christ
d	☑	☐	☐	Detective Constable/ direct current/ District of Columbia/ in-service training
e	☐	☑	☐	
f	☐	☐	☑	mate
g	☑	☐	☐	middle-of-the-road
h	☐	☑	☐	sealed with a loving kiss
i	☐	☐	☑	teaspoon
j	☐	☐	☑	week

5 Stress in English words
▶ **Exercise 28**
1 **syllable** force, four
2 **syllables** famous
3 **syllables** fortunate, formula
4 **syllables** fortunately, unfortunate
5 **syllables** unfortunately

▶ **Exercise 29**
b 'neighbour   c to'morrow
d ˌcompleˈmentary   e aˈrrangement
f 'atmosˌphere   g beˈtween
h surˈprise   i oˈccur
j 'expert   k ˌphotoˈgraphic
l acˌceleˈration

▶ **Exercise 30**
a sixty, photo, image
b sixteen, correct, inform
c fantasy, advertise, educate,
d fantastic, imagine, banana
e advertisement, photography, significant
f information, education, photographic

▶ **Exercise 31**
1 Robyn, beautiful, living, pictures, created, outdoors, foresight, imagination, knowledge, process, gradually, reputation, singular, creative, imaginative

Example answers
2 a Robyn, beautiful, living, pictures, foresight, knowledge, process, gradually, singular
  b created, outdoors, creative, imaginative
  c reputation
    imagination

6 Words that can be both nouns and verbs
▶ **Exercise 32**
☐☐   ☐☐
b noun   verb
c noun   verb
d noun   verb
e noun   verb
f noun   verb
g noun   verb
h noun   verb
i noun   verb

7 Stress in compounds
▶ **Exercise 33**
b 'jet ˌlag   c 'match,box
d ˌfloppy 'disk   e 'book,mark
f 'ice ˌrink   g 'road,side
h ˌmobile 'phone   i 'work,load

Grammar information
1 Word classes
▶ **Exercise 34**
b interjection   c preposition   d adjective
e conjunction   f adjective   g noun
h preposition   i adjective   j interjection
k conjunction   l conjunction   m noun
n preposition

▶ **Exercise 35**
Example answer
Some of the links are to do with before in time, behind in place, not the front; movement away from the front, towards the beginning and backwards.

▶ **Exercise 36**
b verb, face[2]   c number, second[2]
d noun, east[1]   e adjective, just[2]
f noun, do[2]   g adverb, halfway[1]
h interjection, morning[2]

▶ **Exercise 37**
Example answers
a beg, pick, stay, disguise, counsel
b elementary, genuine, pretty, tight, visual
c chiefly, curiously, frankly, ideally, straight
d technology, project, landlord, demand, boat

▶ **Exercise 38**
a 2, 4, 5, 8, 11, 18, 24, 25
b 1, 6, 7, 9, 13, 14, 16, 19
c 3, 10, 12, 15, 17, 20, 21, 22, 23

2 Irregular noun plurals
▶ **Exercise 39**
b hoofs/hooves   c halves
d analyses   e tomatoes
f cargoes   g volcanoes/volcanos
h crises   i chairmen
j phenomena

3 Nouns used in the singular or plural
▶ **Exercise 40**
used only in the plural   c, d, e, h, i, j, s
has a special meaning when used in the plural   b, f, g

4 Countable and uncountable nouns
▶ **Exercise 41**

1 countable [C]	sense number
improvement	2
cigarette	
cloud	2, 3
paper	2, 3, 4, 5
wine	1a, 1b
experience	3

2 uncountable [U]	sense number
luggage	
advice	
knowledge	
paper	1
wine	1, 2
experience	1, 2

3 countable or uncountable [C/U]	sense number
improvement	1
encouragement	
cloud	1
paper	6

6 Prepositions

▶ Exercise 43
b about c from d about e to f in

▶ Exercise 44
Example answers
b I've always been interested in theatre and drama.
c I'm very fond of children.
d My country is famous for its wine.
e I'm very good at maths.
f If you work as a political correspondent, you need to be familiar with international politics.
g I usually feel guilty about not spending enough time with my family.

7 Verb patterns

▶ Exercise 45
b buying c to accept d going e to meet
f to be g going h to get i dressing
j to help

8 Extra help in grammar boxes

▶ Exercise 46
than, that, the, their, theirs, them, themself, themselves, then, there, therefore, they, this, though

▶ Exercise 47
b determiner c pronoun d preposition
e conjunction f pronoun g pronoun
h adjective

▶ Exercise 48
a 2 Before, for b 1 It's 2 its c 1 few 2 a few
d 1 as well/too 2 also e 1 less 2 Fewer

Finding and exploring meanings

1 Finding the correct entry

▶ Exercise 49
b verb, adjective, noun c two d No, it isn't.
e At the end of the entry for limp[2].
f 1 limp[3] 2 limp[1], meaning 1 3 limp[2], meaning 2
  4 limp[2], meaning 2 5 limp[2], meaning 1

▶ Exercise 50
b mine / mine
  1 /maɪn/ 2 /maɪn/
c (read / read)
  1 /riːd/ 2 /red/
d (wind / wind)
  1 /wɪnd/ 2 /waɪnd/
e bear / bear
  1 /beə/ 2 /beə/
f (row / row)
  1 /raʊ/ 2 /rəʊ/
g (tears / tears)
  1 /tɪəz/ 2 /teəz/

2 Long entries

▶ Exercise 51
five

▶ Exercise 52
b 5 c 6 d 4 e 2 f 1

▶ Exercise 53
objects (e.g. hailstones), vehicles (e.g. jeep), people (e.g. baby, kids, band), light, sound (e.g. radar waves), cheque, email message

▶ Exercise 54
a 19 b 1 meaning 3 2 meaning 13 3 meaning 15
4 meaning 6

▶ Exercise 55
a bus, train, car b 6   c twenty minutes
d meaning 6a e meaning 6b f a shop window

▶ Exercise 56

	¹c	o	n	²c	e	³r	n	e	⁴d
	h			o		o			i
	a		⁵s	m	a	l	l		r
	r		i			⁶l			r
	⁷r	u	l	e		⁸l	i	v	e
	a		i			g			c
	⁹c	a	¹⁰p	s		¹¹s	h	o	t
	t		¹²s	h	e	e	t		i
	e		o			a			o
	¹³r	e	c	e	p	t	i	o	n

▶ Exercise 57

¹r	e	²s	u	³l	t		⁴m	⁵e	l	⁶l	o	⁷w
i		t		i				s		o		a
⁸c	o	r	n	e	⁹r		¹⁰s	t	r	a	i	n
h		i			e			a		d		d
¹¹l	a	n	d	e	d			t		¹²e	y	e
y		g		¹³e	x	¹⁴t	e	n	d			r
				e		o						
¹⁵c	o	¹⁶m	m	o	¹⁷n				¹⁸a		¹⁹	
²⁰o	i	l		a				²¹g	e	n	t	l	e
l		o		n				u		t		v
²²u	p	s	e	t	s		²³e	²⁴s	c	a	p	e
m		e		l				e		c		l
²⁵n	o	d	d	e	d		²⁶s	t	a	k	e	s

3 Understanding definitions

▶ Exercise 58
b 4 c 1 d 6 e 2 f 5
Missing word: understand

▶ Exercise 59
a They are all different types of birds.
b
1 falcon; This is the only bird that doesn't live near water.
2 dodo; This is the only bird that doesn't exist any more.
3 condor; This is the only bird that can fly.
4 hummingbird; This is the only very small bird.

▶ Exercise 60
2 a 3 a 4 a 5 c 6 b

▶ Exercise 63
1 face
2
face[1]
1 front of head: 3, 8, 11, 14, 20
2 mountain/building side: 1, 9, 10, 16
4 way sth looks/appears: 2, 4, 13, 23
face[2]
1 be pointing/turned to: 12, 15, 25
2 deal with problem: 5, 7, 18, 22, 24
3 accept: 6, 19, 21
5 have to compete against: 17

▶ Exercise 64

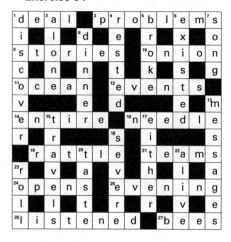

Exploring a dictionary page

▶ Exercise 65
a 2 b correspondent[2], corresponding, correspondingly, corridor, corroborate, corroboration, cortisone, coruscating, the Cosa Nostra, cosign, cosine, cos lettuce
c because d two
e increase, decrease, decline, fall, cortices

▶ Exercise 66
a co'rollary, co'rona, 'coronary, 'coroner
b coronet c corps (singular) /kɔː/ corps (plural) /kɔːz/ d coronation e culture, identity, image, planning, strategy, structure f No, it can't.
g cornet h maize i cornflour, cornflower
j corporate bond, corporate hospitality, corporate raider, corporate welfare
k business and journalism l Cornish pasty
m cornrow n coronary, corpora
o 1 cornstarch, corn syrup, corporate welfare
2 corner shop, cornet, cornflour, Cornish pasty, corporation 3 corollary 4 corporal[2], corporeal
5 cornet 6 cornucopia 7 cornice 8 corona
9 coronary[1], coronary[2], coronary thrombosis
10 corporate bond, corporate raider, corporatism

Collocations, idioms and phrasal verbs

1 Collocations

▶ Exercise 67
b wide, strict, literal, broad c convey, create, develop d contract, price, deal

▶ Exercise 68

Example answers

a
1 bend, bow, cock, duck, incline, lift, lower, nod, shake, tilt, toss
2 accept, authorize, delay, demand, enforce, make, meet, receive, secure, suspend, withhold

b
1 bandy, bare, hairy, long, shapely, slender
2 great, huge, important, major, outstanding, positive, significant, useful, valuable

c
1 attentively, carefully, closely, hard, intently, politely
2 considerably, dramatically, drastically, gradually, greatly, sharply, significantly, substantially

d
1 belief, misconception, myth, opinion, view
2 encounter, glimpse, interlude, moment, nod, pause, period, stay, visit, word

2 Idioms and phrases

▶ Exercise 70

b mind **c** prey **d** matter **e** bearings **f** press
g spot **h** wisdom **i** corner **j** chance **k** mile
l pocket

3 Finding an idiom and phrase

▶ Exercise 71

b At the last meeting I <u>got cold feet</u> and I haven't been since. *foot*
c It's been difficult but now there is <u>light at the end of the tunnel</u>. *light*
d It seems pretty risky, but I think we'll <u>take the plunge</u>. *plunge*
e He's not <u>in her good books</u>. *book*
f It's obvious what you have to do: here it is <u>in black and white</u>. *black-and-white*

▶ Exercise 72

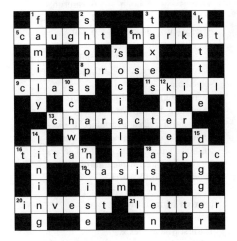

4 Phrasal verbs

▶ Exercise 73

b on **c** out **d** into **e** into **f** in

▶ Exercise 74

b to **c** after **d** after **e** on **f** on
g back

▶ Exercise 75

Example answers

get along, get behind, get up, get away, get out, get across, get into

put on, put up, put away, put out, put across, put into

come on, come along, come up, come away, come out, come across, come into

bring on, bring along, bring up, bring out

turn on, turn up, turn away, turn out, turn into

▶ Exercise 76

(crossword)

▶ Exercise 77

(crossword)

Choosing the right word

1 Style and subject labels

▶ Exercise 78

a spoken **b** formal **c** literary

▶ Exercise 79

a business **b** legal **c** science

▶ Exercise 80

a cricket: over, innings, Test match, series
b golf: hole, driven, bunker, drive
c football: pass, penalty area, shot, goalkeeper, substitute, winger, cross, corner, goal
d tennis: racket string, served, 26-stroke rally, match point, forehand, baseline
e basketball: forward, guard, court, pass, basket, dunked
f swimming: freestyle, medley, backstroke, the butterfly

▶ Exercise 81

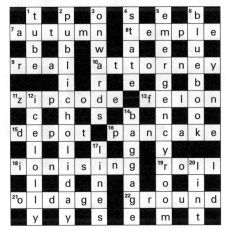

2 Varieties of English

▶ Exercise 82

a Australian **b** Indian **c** Scottish

▶ Exercise 83

British English	American English
petrol station	gas station
car park	parking lot
boot	trunk
windscreen	windshield
bonnet	hood
indicator	turn signal
handbrake	emergency brake
roundabout	traffic circle/rotary
petrol	gasoline

▶ Exercise 84

3 **b** AE **c** BE **d** AE **e** AE **f** BE
  g BE **h** BE **i** AE **j** BE
4 **b** streetcar **c** lift **d** takeout
  e someplace else **f** tap **g** maths
  h CV **i** candy **j** aeroplane

▶ Exercise 85

(crossword)

3 Synonyms

▶ Exercise 86

Example answer

2 how long people travel for; for what purpose or with what aim people travel; how people travel; how many people travel

▶ Exercise 87

b flight   c crossing   d ride   e expedition
f outing   g excursion   h voyage

▶ Exercise 88

advertising

▶ Exercise 89

a exactly/absolutely agree; I couldn't agree more
b I suppose so; I guess so
c I take your point, but …; You have a point, but …; That's true, but …

▶ Exercise 90

b poor/useless
c unpleasant/nasty/horrible
d incompetent/poor
e atrocious/awful/terrible/appalling
f atrocious/awful/terrible/appalling
g severe

▶ Exercise 91

a legendary   b notorious   c celebrity
d eminent

▶ Exercise 92

2

b unstable   c in the right place at the right time
d unsociable   e soft   f liked
g smooth   h humble   i exterior   j false

▶ Exercise 93

A crossword grid with the following filled answers:

here, courageous, saliva, sorcerer, taxi, inhibition, ring, naive, deny, unemployed, pope, obstacle, ornate, artificial, owns

Language study

1 Background information

▶ Exercise 94

a Something that could cause a lot of problems.
b 26 December; it comes from the old custom of giving servants a gift of money called a 'Christmas box'.
c A difficult situation that is impossible to escape from because each part of the problem must be solved first.
d A political leader in the novel *1984*.
e The Prime Minister of the UK.

▶ Exercise 95

1

b net + citizen   c screen + teenager
d documentary + drama   e net + etiquette
f documentary + soap opera

2

1 b   2 d   3 e   4 a   5 f   6 c

2 Metaphors

▶ Exercise 97

1

b happy   c important   d power
e understanding

2

b 5, 8   c 7, 10   d 1, 3   e 4, 9

Exploring a dictionary page

▶ Exercise 98

a Corks are made of cork or sometimes plastic.
b From the bark, the outer covering, of a tree called a cork oak.
c To move in a spiral.
d No, it doesn't. It tastes unpleasant.
e The second syllable: *beef*.
f In British English it means a sweet drink that you mix with water. In American English it means a sweet thick alcoholic drink.
g In British English it means crops such as wheat and barley. In American English it means the seeds of a corn plant.
h There are four red words: core^1, core^2, corn and corner^1.
i corner^1
j Three: corgi, cormorant and corncrake.
k cords
l off
m seven
n at, in, of
o In architecture.
p at the corner, in the corner, right-hand corner, left-hand corner, on the corner, turn the corner, street corner, the four corners of the earth/globe/world, tight corner, back/force someone into a corner

Working with texts

▶ Exercise 99

a jail
b No, it doesn't. *Prisoner* means someone who is in prison; *jailer* means someone whose job is to guard the people in prison.
c prisoner of conscience
d a prison term/sentence
e 1 remand   2 stand   3 guilty
f 1 a sheet of glass, metal, paper, plastic
  2 a splinter of glass, wood
  3 a pane of glass
g Meaning 5: punishment for doing something wrong or illegal.
h It is used for saying that strange or unfair things sometimes happen.
i strange, unusual
j Meaning 1e: no longer in prison.
k Yes, it could. They both mean the same.

l *Sentence* has three meanings:
  1 a group of words that expresses a statement, question or instruction
  2 a punishment given by a judge
  3 when a judge sentences someone, they officially state what someone's punishment will be
  Sentence is a red word.

▶ Exercise 100

a

nouns: American Indian, chief, recollector, sage, man
adjectives: grey, gnarled, old, antique, ancient
b recollect, collector
c cross someone's hand with silver
d They collect postage stamps.
e 1 enigmatic   2 moth-eaten
  3 scramble   4 serene
f egg, on page 446
g limey, Brit
h The word *limey* is an old-fashioned word and it is used mainly in American English. The word *Brit* is an informal word.
i Ten words: gnarled, gnash, gnashers, gnashing, gnat, gnaw, gnawing, gnome, gnomic, gnu. The letter 'g' is not pronounced in these words.
j tepee
k Meaning 4: the whole of a number or amount that you have just mentioned.
l The heritage trail: Wild West ghost towns, War of Independence landmarks, Japanese car manufacturers.
m Meaning 6: someone that you are responsible for and take care of.

▶ Exercise 101

a Meaning 2: a large deep hole that appears to have no bottom.
b 1 heart   2 lungs   3 spleen
  4 limbs   5 brain   6 eardrums
c 1 beat   2 crush   3 splurge (out)
  4 force (out)   5 tick over   6 burst
d They imply sudden and strong changes.
e Meaning 2c: used for emphasizing an extreme place or time, for example at the top or the end of something.
f eyeful, armful, handful, fistful, mouthful
  an eyeful of dust, an eyeful of soapy water
  an armful of clothes, an armful of books
  a handful of coins, a handful of stones
  a fistful of lottery tickets, a fistful of papers
  a mouthful of food, a mouthful of water
g A long and difficult search.
h It means that the diver is right on the edge between living and dying.
i ascend
j The first syllable: /rekɔːd/
k hold your breath
l breath
m abyss, the depths
  They are both used in literary contexts. The word *abyss* can also be used in a journalistic context to refer to a very frightening or dangerous situation, or one in which there seems to be no hope.
n dedicate
o vein, artery